# RISE AND THRIVE

A Guide for Transforming Your Mood,
Cultivating Inspiration, and Living
Vibrantly with Chronic Illness

MASUMI GOLDMAN

http://www.riseandthrivebooks.com/

ISBN 9781734188707
eISBN 9781734188714

# Get Your FREE Gift Now!

# READ THIS FIRST:

As a gift for buying my book, I would like to give you the *Rise and Thrive Workbook.*

Your FREE workbook includes printable journaling pages and a checklist with 40 additional tips to continue thriving.

# GET YOUR WORKBOOK HERE:

https://riseandthrivebooks.com/workbook

# DEDICATION

For those of you who have bravely walked this difficult road of chronic pain, this book is for you.

For those of you who have been told that your symptoms are psychosomatic, this book is for you.

For those of you who have spent exorbitant amounts of time and money going from doctor to doctor in search of a proper diagnosis, this book is for you.

For those of you who have been told that "you don't look sick," this book is for you.

For those of you who have felt excluded, alone, and misunderstood in this journey, this book is for you.

For those of you who have lost hope, found hope, or find yourselves somewhere in-between, this book is for you.

Wherever you are in your journey with chronic illness, this book is for you.

# TABLE OF CONTENTS

*Section One*
## BOOSTERS

*Section Two*
## BUILDERS

*Section Three*
## TROUBLESHOOTING & FINAL THOUGHTS

*Introduction*

# YOU CAN THRIVE

The problem with chronic illness is that you lose so much control—control over your body, control over the diagnosis, control over the pain, control over your independence, and control over pretty much every aspect of your life.

It's depressing.

You give up activities that cause you pain, and you postpone your hopes, dreams, and plans because you are exhausted.

You gradually lose your purpose, and one day you wake up to the grim realization that you don't like your life anymore. Nothing about it resembles the life that you've imagined for yourself.

You know in your heart that you want to escape the apathetic, uninspired mindset that's now a part of your existence, but you don't know how.

If you're going through all of this right now, let me tell you that I've been there too. I've suffered, and I've felt the hopelessness of having to give up so much of my life.

But guess what? I discovered the secret to turning it all around.

It took years of trial and error, but I developed a system that pulled me out of the darkness and reignited a fire within me. I am happier today than I've ever been.

I've set new goals for myself and actually achieved a lifelong dream of publishing a book. It's funny that I managed to accomplish this now, but I didn't have the discipline and drive to get it done when my physical body felt great. I attribute this success to the program I describe in the coming chapters.

If you follow the plan that I've laid out in this book, I am confident that you will rise out of indifference and negativity and begin to thrive, too.

Maybe your life goals and aspirations will be different than the ones you had before your chronic illness diagnosis, but who cares? Different doesn't mean inferior. They will be new, inspired goals.

You might not be able to change your diagnosis, but you can regain control over the trajectory of your future, and you'll have the energy to plan a life that you want to live.

You do NOT have to be cured in order to live an inspired, fulfilled life.

Get ready to RISE AND THRIVE!

## Chapter 1

# FROM PAIN TO PURPOSE

One evening, not so long ago, I crawled into bed and surrounded myself with a sea of pillows to help support my aching body.

I gingerly placed one pillow under my swollen right knee, two behind me to support my neck and back, and one on each side of me to create a safety barrier to protect against a sleeping husband that might roll into me from the left and enthusiastic children that might jump onto the bed from the right.

My body hurt badly, and I felt very discouraged.

For years, I was led to believe that these terrible aches and pains were caused by some unknown, generic autoimmune condition.

Today, I have more answers and know that Lyme disease, which went undiagnosed and untreated for many years, was the cause of my mysterious pain.

What began as a treatable illness that was transmitted to me by an infected deer tick morphed into a chronic autoimmune condition that continues to be difficult to cure today.

Most of the time, my symptoms are well controlled, and I feel good. Once in a while, I experience random, unpredictable autoimmune attacks that affect my joints, muscles, tendons, and ligaments.

On this particular evening when I barricaded myself within a pillow cocoon, I wasn't well enough to exercise, cook, or do anything that I considered productive. Yet, I felt restless. I decided in that moment that I should read some motivational quotes to lift my spirits.

Maybe I didn't have the energy to do anything right then and there, but I reasoned that reading a series of inspirational quotes might give me the boost that I needed to attempt some exercise or cooking the next day.

I grabbed my phone and started searching online for an inspirational message that might offer me some hope and motivation to keep up the good fight. That's when I found this:

"The only person you should be in competition with is the person you were yesterday."

The quote seemed inspirational enough, and I loved that the message encouraged me to look inward rather than compare myself to others, BUT...

I was in the middle of a painful flare. I was past the point of comparing myself to others. Unfortunately, I was not past the point of falling into a funk by comparing myself to the healthy, active person I used to be. I suddenly felt hopeless.

How could I be in competition with a former version of myself when I couldn't even put any weight onto my right leg?

I used to run and do push-ups and hours of intense yoga and handstands. And there I was, surrounded by a sea of pillows with a busted knee that prevented me from walking. My wrists and forearms were on fire. Forget doing push-ups—I could barely push myself up out of bed!

## MY DEFINING MOMENT

As a stream of self-imposed negative thoughts bombarded me, I suddenly became intensely aware of who I was and what I was battling.

It wasn't just a chronic autoimmune illness. The illness was a constant fight in the background, but the more pressing battle was the one taking place in my mind.

I could either succumb to the negative thoughts and believe the mental chatter telling me that I was a shadow of the person I once was, or I could beat those thoughts into a pulp and rise up.

---

"The things you think about determine the quality of your mind. Your soul takes on the color of your thoughts."

### -Marcus Aurelius

---

I decided in that moment that I would fight hard. I would make it my purpose to thrive, no matter what hit me next. I would win the battle against draining, negative self-talk and exhausting apathy toward life. Even though I knew it would be tough in the face of a new autoimmune attack, I was committed.

Once I figured out how to win this battle in my mind, I would make it my life's mission to share that method with others.

That decision was the seed that ultimately grew into this book that you're holding in your hands. This book is the culmination of five years of trial and error to determine what was most effective and doable in the face of my own unpredictable, debilitating pain.

Now that I know what works well at combating mental fatigue, negativity, and hopelessness, I want to spread that knowledge. I know that there are others experiencing similar physical and emotional struggles.

With over a hundred autoimmune illnesses in existence, plus chronic conditions like fibromyalgia and chronic fatigue syndrome, we're talking about more than 60 million Americans dealing with chronic conditions. I'm not alone, and neither are you.

## HOW THIS BOOK CAN HELP YOU

One thing you should know up front is that this is <u>NOT</u> a how-to-heal manual.

While we will discuss some best methods for keeping your physical body feeling good, that is not the focus of this book. If that's what you're looking for, head to the bookstore and you'll find several books that discuss various protocols and diets to heal the body. You'll also be able to find a variety of cookbooks that explain how to create healing meals and reduce systemic inflammation.

This book will not specifically address how to *reduce* your pain, but it will teach you how to stay motivated to live your best life, *despite* your pain.

My focus here is to work on the inside—to help you eliminate the negativity and indifference that creep into your mind when you are living with an exhausting chronic illness. You can improve your mood and harness your new energy to live the life you want for yourself.

This is not a how-to-heal manual. It's a how-to-thrive manual.

## SURVIVING VS. THRIVING

When I began outlining the chapters for this book, I knew immediately that it could not be branded as a survival guide for people living with chronic illnesses. I wanted more for myself and more for you than just survival.

In my mind, the word *survival* didn't conjure images of vibrant life. Survival seemed synonymous with "just getting by."

I didn't want to just get by. I wanted to leave survival in the dust and embrace a life where thriving was the norm. The fact that you're reading this book leads me to believe that you feel the same way.

There is a big difference between thriving and surviving.

When you are simply **surviving,** you tolerate your life and your illness with the intention of just making it to the next day. You lack the ambition and drive to live well—not because you're lazy—but because your body and mind are exhausted. The battle to reclaim a healthy life seems impossibly difficult, and the heaviness of this realization spills into all aspects of your life.

I get it. It's easy to get caught up in the whirlwind of managing a chronic illness. I've spent more hours than I can count working through the various facets of my disease: scheduling doctors' appointments, calling insurance companies, filling out claim forms, taking supplements, researching new pain relief remedies, going to physical therapy, and reading just about every available resource to learn more about healing.

It's exhausting. Finding the energy to move forward in life while handling all of the usual day-to-day responsibilities of paying bills and managing a household can be daunting.

But, if I've learned anything in my multiyear journey with an autoimmune illness, it's that the difference between surviving and thriving is a distinction that is made in the mind.

When you are **thriving**, you feel hopeful and driven, and you refuse to be limited by physical conditions.

You wake up with a sense of purpose, despite the pain.

You have the will and desire to meet with holistic healers, find online support groups, start a meditation practice, attend yoga classes, learn about the healing power of alternative therapies, overhaul your diet, and share your experiences to help and inspire others facing similar challenges.

Any given day may be marked by physical discomfort, but that pain doesn't keep you from living a vibrant, fulfilled life.

You are not in denial.

You accept your current reality of having a chronic condition, but your outlook on life is bright and your mindset is one that is marked by peace, stability, and inspiration to live well.

Given the choice between surviving and thriving, I think we would all choose thriving. My goal is to show you how to get there.

Your time here on this beautiful earth is limited, and moving around in survival mode day after day is unacceptable. You deserve better.

## Chapter 2

# GET READY FOR TRANSFORMATION

I hope you are starting to feel something stirring inside of you—an excitement to reclaim your life and a desire to climb out of the survival rut and start thriving!

The idea behind this book is to capture that spark of excitement and build real, lasting transformation.

---

"Transformation isn't a future event,
it's a present-day activity."

**-Jillian Michaels**

---

Whether you've been diagnosed with rheumatoid arthritis, chronic Lyme disease, lupus, psoriatic arthritis, Crohn's disease, Sjögren's syndrome, ulcerative colitis, fibromyalgia, chronic fatigue syndrome, or any of the many other chronic conditions out there, you must remember that you are not your disease.

Your illness doesn't define you.

Many people suffering from chronic conditions think that their lives will really begin once they feel good. They put their hopes and dreams on the back burner and tell themselves that everything on their to-do list will get done when their illnesses resolve.

Would you believe me if I told you that your life doesn't have to be on hold?

When you have a chronic condition, every day isn't going to be ideal, but your life can still be meaningful and productive. You don't have to be cured to start living.

You can remain motivated, have the right mindset to live well, and achieve your dreams while feeling good about yourself.

My hope for you is that after reading this book and implementing the suggestions, you will experience transformation in one or more of the following ways:

o   You will change the way you view your illness and your potential to live well.

o   You will regain hope if it is currently lost and recognize that you have the power to create your own happiness.

o   You will take steps to create an environment of positivity so that you can shine.

o   You will understand that you still have plenty of control over the direction of your life, despite the unpredictability of your illness.

o   You will keep your eyes on your own game because you are in competition with no one else.

o   You will learn to embrace the present rather than lamenting the past. By changing your mindset and rekindling your sense of hope, you will change how you live your life.

## COMING TO TERMS WITH YOUR ILLNESS

Some of you reading this book have been on the chronic illness journey for many years. Others have been recently diagnosed, and if you fall into this camp, you might need to give yourself a minute to absorb the news.

I know I was in a state of disbelief when I was first diagnosed with an autoimmune condition. I didn't believe it because I really thought I had a sports injury.

I originally went to a podiatrist because I thought my hips and feet hurt from the repetitive motion of running on my treadmill each day. I expected a set of orthotics to insert into my shoes and maybe some advice to lay off the running for a while. I even met with a sports medicine doctor and began weekly physical therapy sessions.

A sports injury was something that my mind could comprehend. It was something that fit into the framework of my life.

Why would I expect anything other than what appeared to be a structural issue? I was active, I ate healthy meals, I had no history of strange illnesses, and even my family medical history was pristine.

When my blood work revealed elevated antibody levels that are typically consistent with rheumatoid arthritis, I was suddenly thrust into a scary, unknown territory. I was completely unprepared and had to shift from the mindset of "sports injury" to "autoimmune disease."

Not only did I feel overwhelmed and scared, but I felt like a failure. All of my efforts to live a healthy life felt wasted.

I ate organic vegetables, stayed away from processed foods, exercised regularly, and I still ended up with some unknown, incurable autoimmune condition that no doctor could predict or easily identify.

I felt like I failed.

I felt like my body betrayed me.

If you find yourself in a similar situation right now and you're experiencing every emotion under the sun, don't beat yourself up. It's OK to feel scared, angry, sad, panicked, or hopeless. It's normal to want to be reclusive and withdraw.

You don't want to wallow in self-pity for an extended length of time, but you do want to allow yourself the space to come to terms with your new reality. A medical diagnosis can be devastating, especially when you visit the doctor with what you think is a minor ailment.

## THE KEY TO A POSITIVE MINDSET

Shortly after I was diagnosed with this autoimmune condition, someone told me to "keep my chin up."

I didn't take it very well.

I was confused, angry, sad, worried about the future, and in constant pain. My ego couldn't handle receiving advice about staying positive from someone who wasn't even struggling with an illness. I was in defensive mode at that time, for sure.

Did this person think I wanted to mope around every day?

Why would I choose to feel negative?

What did they know about struggling with something so serious?

What did they know about being told about the possibility of becoming disabled?

I felt enraged.

How is it helpful to tell anyone in pain to stay positive?

It's hard enough to be in pain on a daily basis, but the feelings of anger and frustration are even more overwhelming when you are unable to achieve the positive mindset that friends and relatives suggest.

It is downright discouraging to be told that a positive mindset is important to heal.

A positive mindset doesn't just materialize because a well-meaning friend or relative tells you to maintain a sunny outlook on life. There is no positivity switch that can be turned on and off like a light.

I went through some serious growing pains during this time in my life. I had to do a lot of soul searching and exploration to figure out how to get through this new reality. I knew I wanted to heal from the physical pain, but even more than that, I wanted to live a happy, motivated life that was filled with purpose.

**What I discovered was that the most effective way to cultivate a positive outlook was to engage in repetitive activities that promoted positivity—habits that didn't require a positive mindset to begin, but ones that ultimately created a brighter outlook just by doing them regularly.**

I discovered that daily mood-boosting habits were the key to a positive mindset.

## EXPERIENCING THE SHIFT

The habits presented in this book are a collection of the daily tasks that I've found to be most effective at helping me cultivate positivity in my own life.

I didn't come up with these habits all at once. It's been a long process of trying a habit, living with it for a while, and then deciding whether or not to keep it in my routine. I realized that not every habit cultivated a positive mindset, and not every habit worked well on days when I had pain.

I kept track of the habits that I could complete on any given day, regardless of pain levels, and I ultimately pieced together a routine that worked well for me.

My carefully curated habits uplifted my spirit, not only because they were inherently uplifting, but because the act of successfully completing them on a daily basis gave me a sense of accomplishment.

The feeling of being productive in a small way brought me happiness. I proved that I was still capable of keeping promises to myself and achieving goals—even if they seemed like insignificant little tasks.

Once I was in the groove of consistently performing my mood-boosting habits, I felt something inside of me shift.

I no longer felt angry or fearful. Instead, I was focused on the experiences I created with my new habits, and those experiences were uplifting.

I learned that developing a positive outlook in the midst of hardship is a self-driven process and a conscious daily decision to do the necessary work to stay positive.

I now know that the successful completion of daily uplifting habits sparks the drive to live a fulfilled, inspired life. You can also achieve this kind of life, despite the emotional and physical setbacks of painful flare-ups.

## MAKE THE COMMITMENT

If you want to begin living with hope for your future and excitement about what lies ahead, you must make a decision.

Are you willing to change your daily routine and take the necessary steps each day to develop a positive mindset?

This requires a commitment on your part. You have to change your ways to change your life. Self-improvement and personal development books don't work unless you take action to improve and develop. If you act, you will transform.

If you are ready to commit, let's move forward together!

**REVIEW TIME:**

You can't talk yourself into a positive mindset, but you CAN do the work to develop one.

The act of achieving small goals each day builds confidence and a strong sense of accomplishment.

You can spark the drive to live an inspired life with daily, uplifting habits.

*Chapter 3*

# HOW THE PROGRAM WORKS

Even if you can't imagine it now, it really is possible to create a life that supersedes the existence you had before your diagnosis. Maybe your life won't look the same, but your goal shouldn't be to restore what you had before. Set your sights higher.

---

The best time to plant a tree was 20 years ago.
The second best time is now.

**-Chinese Proverb**

---

With this program, you can rise out of the funk, leave apathy behind, and begin to thrive in a way that you've never thrived before. It will take commitment and patience as you add intentional tasks to your routine in a two-phase program.

Phase One consists of eight daily habits that will cultivate the excitement and discipline to create an inspired life. Your entire mindset will shift during this phase of the program for two reasons.

First, the habits themselves are healthy, uplifting practices. Second, the act of successfully incorporating all eight habits into your life every single day is rewarding and, therefore, uplifting. Setting goals and achieving them is a big part of being happy.

Phase Two builds upon the momentum of Phase One with eight additional suggestions for healthy living. You can think of these suggestions as being the recommended building blocks to help you grow into your newly inspired life.

With your daily habits in place and your building blocks laid, you are ready to thrive. The sky is the limit.

Let's discuss the details.

## PHASE ONE: BOOSTERS

In the first phase of the program, you will perform eight tasks every day for 40 days, regardless of your current state of health. Because you will be performing these tasks daily, they will become natural habits.

Even if your body hurts and your mobility is limited, I am confident that you will be able to do them all.

These habits are called "Boosters" because they are meant to boost your mood and help you develop the positive, inspired spirit that you need to build the life of your dreams.

You might think that you can't commit to doing anything on a daily basis because you don't feel well enough. This is where you need to take a leap of faith and trust that you will be fine.

In this phase of the program, I will not ask you to exercise each day or get in the kitchen to prepare all of your meals. I know that your days are unpredictable and your pain and energy levels are variable.

Don't worry—you will be able to get through the Boosters regardless of how you're feeling. If you feel down in the dumps and not very energetic, you might be skeptical of this entire plan. You don't have to believe in it or be in a good mood to get started.

Do it anyway. Focus on taking action and performing the Boosters every day. Not only will you be uplifted by the Boosters themselves, but you will be uplifted by the act of successfully completing them.

Going through the Boosters, one by one, one day at a time, is your goal. Don't underestimate the mood-boosting effect of simply doing what you said you would do.

Remember that it's much easier to cultivate a positive mindset than it is to convince yourself of one. Do the program. It's a systematic approach.

## WHY 40 DAYS?

At this point, you might be curious about the length of the program. According to yogic philosophy, it takes 40 days to break a destructive habit or to develop a new, healthy habit. Since I happen to be a yoga teacher, this 40-day time frame resonates with me.

In my own life, I've been able to break habits (like a sugar addiction) and create new habits (like a daily meditation practice) within 40 days. I think 40 days is the right length of time to get you on track as well.

Showing up every day for 40 days is significant. Even though it's less than six weeks, it's long enough to experience a complete shift in mindset.

If 40 days sounds incredibly long and overwhelming, dig down deep and do it anyway. You don't have to muster up physical strength because the Boosters don't require it. It's all mental strength.

Hold yourself accountable. No excuses. Through repetition and daily commitment, the Boosters will become habits that feel natural.

By performing these mood-boosting activities, you will develop the positive, energized mindset that is needed to build an inspired life. You will also have the energy to perform the activities in the next phase of the program.

## PHASE TWO: BUILDERS

After 40 days, you will move on to the second phase of the program. The idea behind Phase Two is to build upon the discipline and excitement that you've created during Phase One.

You've developed a positive mindset by performing the Boosters each day, and you've built the confidence to know that you are capable of sticking to a program.

You will continue performing all of the Boosters each day and now add some new tasks to your routine that will enhance your life and boost your enthusiasm and energy levels. The eight tasks presented in the second phase are called "Builders," and they are meant to serve as the foundation for your newly inspired life.

Many of the Builders will require you to feel good in body and mind. This is why it's so important to successfully complete the first 40 days of this program before moving on. The Builders will challenge you, so you need to be in a good place mentally and emotionally before you add more to your daily plate.

Unlike the eight Boosters, which are a required part of the program, all eight Builders are suggestions. They should not create stress and they don't all have to be done on a daily basis.

If you're not able to incorporate a certain activity into your life, skip it. My hope is that you ultimately try everything. Keep what works for you and let go of the rest.

Start by adding one Builder at a time, and successfully incorporate it into your life for a full week before taking on another new Builder. Do not be discouraged if you aren't feeling well and can't do all of the items on the list. The Builders aren't going anywhere, and you can add them to your life whenever you are up to it.

The goal is not to overwhelm you with action items but to give you hope and inspiration for a life that you are excited to live.

Remember that your medical condition may be chronic and recurring, but it is not static. It is variable in nature, and what is impossible today may be doable tomorrow.

Keep trying. Don't give up!

There is no end date for Phase Two. This is the beginning of the rest of your life.

## LIFE BEYOND PHASE TWO

It's a bit counterintuitive, but by adding the Builders into your daily routine on top of the existing Boosters, you will have the sense that you actually have more time to pursue what you love rather than less.

Not only will you have the sense of increased time, but you will also have the sense of increased energy.

Because your energy and desire for a purpose-filled life will be at an all-time high, you will find yourself considering new projects and hobbies that you didn't think you had time for in the past.

Allow yourself to explore these new endeavors and keep an open mind. It is in this mindset, once you have made it through the Boosters and Builders, that new ideas will take root and new goals will emerge. Embrace your new life!

### REVIEW TIME:

Setting goals and achieving them is a big part of being happy.

Commit to all eight Boosters every single day for 40 days to create an inspired mindset.

After 40 days, add one Builder to your routine for a week. Choose to keep it or let it go. Repeat this process with the other seven Builders. Keep doing all of your daily Boosters during this time.

*Section One*

# BOOSTERS

*Chapter 4*

# THINK FAST

Are you ready to get started? Let's do this!

By committing to a list of eight daily tasks called Boosters, you will change your outlook on life. You will begin to notice that your thoughts and energy feel brighter. You will feel positive about what you've accomplished, and you will be inspired to do more. Read through all eight Boosters and commit to them for 40 days.

This first Booster is a great way to jumpstart the program because it requires you to take action only once, and then you're all set for the length of the program. Set it and forget it. It's a simple task, but not necessarily an easy one.

## Booster #1: Commit to a social media fast.

No Facebook. No Instagram. No Twitter. No Snapchat. Nothing. Delete every app that can be classified as social media from your phone so that you're not tempted to break your fast. Don't even think about logging into your accounts from a computer.

Commit to a minimum of 40 days without social media, and then assess at the end of that time frame whether you will continue with your fast or whether you will begin adding social media back into your life.

Why am I adamant about removing all social media as part of your jumpstart plan to shift your outlook?

I am adamant because I want <u>YOU</u> to be in control over the messages and images that you consume on a regular basis.

If you are not feeling well and you are in a season of your life where you can't get around easily or aren't able to work, watching other peoples' lives through the lens of social media may cause you to feel frustrated, angry, sad, lonely, hopeless, and question your own purpose in life.

Social media is not helpful in creating the right mindset for you to be able to move forward in your own space at your own pace.

The whole point of doing the eight daily rituals is to cultivate a mindset that is conducive to healing and thriving in a positive atmosphere. You lose all control of that carefully crafted mindset when you scroll through thousands of posts that are created by other people.

## THE HIGHLIGHT REEL

Remember that social media (for the most part) is a place where people aren't posting their challenges or their insecurities. They are sharing their best moments in life.

You're seeing the marathons that they are running.

The healthy meals that they are cooking from scratch on a weeknight.

The goals that they are crushing.

The vacations that they are taking.

You're seeing how they wake up at 5:00 a.m. to conquer the world before everyone else is awake.

You see all of their athletic feats and you hear about all of their achievements at work, school, and in all aspects of their life.

You are not seeing the unpaid bills, the marital struggles, or any of the failures.

Even though you might miss seeing photos of your friends' kids and pets during your 40-day fast, your mindset will benefit greatly by putting yourself back into the driver's seat.

You will not be a passive consumer of other people's online posts. Instead, you will be the one actively choosing the books, blogs, and podcasts that you consume during this time. We will discuss this further in the next chapter.

## THE DESTRUCTIVE COMPARISON GAME

You also won't be tempted to play the comparison game with your social media friends and followers because you've removed all opportunities to compare.

I've been on this autoimmune journey for several years now, and I've learned that comparing yourself to other people when you are in the midst of healing is a really bad idea. You really don't want to go down that road.

Comparing yourself to others who don't have health challenges can lead to depression, feelings of hopelessness, and feelings of failure about your own life. It's not fair to do this to yourself, and it doesn't put you in the right mindset to be able to live well.

Doesn't it figure that we all tend to compare ourselves to others when we are feeling our worst?

We lie in bed, aching, and even though it hurts to move, we start comparing our abilities to those of a friend who goes to the gym every day. Or maybe we start thinking about work and the energetic colleague who seems to be climbing the corporate ladder at breakneck speed.

We start to feel angry about our health and how our bodies are failing us. Then the jealousy starts to set in. We can no longer feel joy for others because we are so consumed with our own shortcomings. And finally, the rhetorical questions begin:

"Why me?"
"Why not her/him?"
"What if I never get better?"
"What if everyone surpasses me while I'm tending to my sick body?"
"Does everyone think I'm a loser?"

Now I have to ask you…Does any of this seem productive? Do you think this is good for your health in any way?

## ELIMINATE THE TRIGGERS

If you want to get yourself to an emotional state where you are thriving, I have no doubt that you can get there. For now, it's important to eliminate the triggers that have you questioning your worth because you are playing the comparison game.

It really doesn't matter what others are doing and how quickly they are doing it. You will see that very clearly if you remove yourself from Facebook, Instagram, Snapchat, Twitter, and any other social media platforms that you use to peer into the lives of others.

How does the idea of a 40-day social media fast sound to you? Can you commit to it? What's making you hesitate?

## EXCUSES, EXCUSES

When I've asked friends whether they would consider a social media fast, they've argued that they need to stay on social media because it's their way of interacting with the people that are meaningful in their lives.

If that's how you feel, shut down your social media anyway, and take an old-fashioned approach.

Call, text, or write letters to your dear friends and family members. If they live in a different country and texting isn't an option, interact on an international messaging app like WhatsApp, Telegram, or Viber. Have true one-on-one conversations with your friends and family. You will find these much more inspiring than just logging into a social media platform and watching someone else's highlight reel.

If your objection to a social media fast is work-related, I understand that you can't cut it out completely. I bet you can still do a lot to cut down on the mindless scrolling though.

Go ahead and remove all social media apps with web versions from your phone. If you need to access each platform from your computer in order to engage, you're less likely to use it for personal reasons. You will begin to associate social media with work, and you'll only use it at your desk. It will no longer be a leisure activity.

I took a solid break from social media because I knew that I wanted to nurture my mind to believe without a doubt that I could lead a healthy, vibrant life, despite my illness.

In order to stay positive and focused on my healing, I needed to be shielded from my social media accounts. I couldn't risk scrolling through my social media feeds and seeing posts that made me feel bad about myself because I was comparing my life to everyone else's curated highlight reels.

Today, I'm back on social media because I'm in a good place emotionally and enjoy the time I spend on a variety of group pages and forums. But, any time I feel an inkling of negativity creeping into my mind, I shut down the accounts and take a break.

I've learned that leaving social media is a quick way to end the stream of negative thoughts and free up massive amounts of time to do worthwhile things to improve my life.

## RETURNING TO SOCIAL MEDIA

If at the end of 40 days, you would like to reintroduce social media back into your life, be very intentional about it.

Be as intentional as you would be with any other hobby that you want to fit into your life. No one pulls out a sewing machine to sew for ten minutes every hour. No one stops working to play tennis for ten minutes every hour.

As a hobby, set aside a special block of time to enjoy it fully. Compartmentalize it, just like a hobby. If you think you need an hour of social media a day, schedule it into a single session at a specific time.

Don't allow it to become the primary source of information and inspiration that fills your mind. You have a new life to build!

## REFLECTIONS & OBSERVATIONS:

<u>DAY 1:</u>

What is your immediate reaction to the idea of a social media fast? Do you feel a sense of anxiety? Excitement? Indifference? Anger? Reluctance to implement this Booster into your life? Take a moment to record your thoughts. What steps will you take to make this Booster a successful reality?

_____

_____

_____

_____

_____

_____

<u>DAY 40:</u>

How do you feel after your 40-day social media fast? Do you feel more in tune with your own goals and aspirations? Do you feel like you have more time each day because you eliminated mindless scrolling? Will you reintroduce social media into your life?

_____

_____

_____

_____

_____

_____

*Chapter 5*

# INSPIRATION OVERLOAD

Once you eliminate social media from your life for 40 days, you will be shocked at how much time you suddenly have for other hobbies and activities.

By eliminating the constant stream of images, status updates, and advertisements, your mind will be a blank slate, ready and available to absorb new information.

The logical next step of this program is to fill that blank slate with creative, inspiring thoughts and topics. The idea is to crowd out negativity, jealousy, and preoccupation with other peoples' lives on social media and fill your mind with ideas that spark a light within you. You are creating the launch pad for a thriving mindset.

To get started, you will need a free block of time as well as an open, receptive mind.

**Booster #2: Spend at least 15 minutes a day immersing yourself in a podcast, blog, or book on any topic that inspires you.**

Let these sources of media be about any and every aspect of life that you enjoy—building a business, home improvement, time management, wealth management, productivity, beauty, history, food, etc.

The key to creating a positive mindset is to find sources of inspiration and bombard yourself with them every single day. These sources of inspiration do not have to be related to healing or wellness. Not everyone is in the mood to read or listen to podcasts about food, hydration, or healing modalities, especially when their life already revolves around these things.

## GETTING STARTED

Start out by going to the bookstore and walk through each aisle. If you don't have a brick-and- mortar store in your area, browse your favorite online resource for books.

Peruse whatever topics appeal to you and discover what your natural interests are. See what books you are naturally inclined to flip through.

I always find myself drawn to beautiful vegetarian cookbooks. I love looking at all of the colorful photographs of healthy meals made with fresh fruits, vegetables, grains, and beans.

Even if I don't have the energy to ever cook a single item in the book, I feel a sense of excitement and potential when I read the recipes and see the photos. It's almost as if it helps me envision a life where I'm so healthy and active that I can create these delicious looking meals every day.

I'm also drawn to the home and garden section of the bookstore. I love to read home organization and decluttering manuals. The thought of beautifying my home just by straightening up what I already have makes me happy! Even when I was a kid, I remember the sense of accomplishment I felt after decluttering and cleaning the small desk in my bedroom. I was convinced that my mind was sharper if the top of my desk was clear of clutter and the surface was smooth from being wiped down.

I might not have the energy to clean out the garage or reorganize the pantry on any given day, but flipping through the pages of a decluttering book gives me a sense of excitement and motivation.

You should be chasing this sense of excitement and motivation in your own book choices.

## BOOKS AND BLOGS

Once you are done exploring the bookstore and know what topics excite you, buy a few books to bring home. Leave them in a prominent place so that you can read whenever the mood strikes.

If a stack of new books isn't in your monthly budget, don't worry. Take a photo of each book that interests you and head to your local library with the photos of your selections. Most public libraries allow you to borrow several books at a time, and you can always go back to swap the books for new ones. Many libraries also have digital versions of books that you can load to your tablet or Kindle for free.

Once you have a selection of books that makes you happy, check online to see if your favorite authors have online blogs that you can follow on a regular basis. If not, do an internet search for the most popular blogs that cover the topics that you enjoy reading about the most.

If you want to spend your 15 minutes catching up with your favorite bloggers each day, then go ahead and do that. If you end up deciding that you prefer reading shorter blog posts each day rather than chapters of longer books, that's fine. Feel free to choose blogs over books. It doesn't really matter.

The idea is to fill your mind briefly each day with topics that spark something within you.

## LISTEN TO INSPIRATION

In addition to your reading choices, find a few different podcasts that motivate and inspire you. Ask your friends for podcast recommendations if you don't know where to start, or spend an evening listening to a bunch of different podcasts on your phone to see what makes you feel good.

I started listening to podcasts after stumbling across an entrepreneurial podcast. The host of the show was an entrepreneur who struggled to build his business for nearly a decade, but now his company is generating hundreds of millions of dollars in sales each year.

His enthusiasm for his work was contagious, and it made me want to listen to him every day. I wasn't even trying to launch a new business, but I loved the passion he had for his work as well as for helping others be their best.

He had hundreds of recordings that ranged from ten minutes long to over an hour and a half long. Depending on the day, and depending on what I was doing, I would pick a different length episode.

If I was driving by myself in the car for 20 minutes, I would listen to a 15-minute episode. If I was short on time and wanted to get through the slower parts of an episode quickly, I would listen at 1.5x the speed. If I was feeling low on energy and needed to stay in bed all day, I would listen to a longer episode that allowed me to close my eyes and listen for an hour or two.

Podcasts have really saved the day during flare-ups. I've had flare-ups of my illness that left me so sick that I couldn't even open my eyes. There have been days when reading wasn't an option because my head hurt and I felt too drained to focus on the pages of a book.

Fortunately, my hearing has always been perfect, so even when I've been completely laid up in bed for days, I've been able to listen to podcasts and fill my mind with positive messages.

## SCHEDULING YOUR 15-MINUTES OF INSPIRATION

Think about your daily schedule and decide when you plan to read or listen to your podcast each day. You must be intentional about this ritual because the day flies by quickly, and you don't want to find yourself crawling into bed at night, closing your eyes to go to sleep and then realizing that you forgot to do your 15 minutes of reading or listening.

Maybe you're an early riser and can do some reading before breakfast. Maybe you want to listen to podcasts on your daily commute. Do you have time after dinner? Or when you take a midday break to drink your coffee or tea? Go through your schedule and figure out when you'll incorporate this ritual.

Remember: You only need a minimum of 15 minutes to successfully complete your daily Booster, but this is not a cap.

Feel free to read or listen for longer periods of time if you want, but make sure that you have a solid 15-minute block of time before you get started.

The impact is just not the same if you read five minutes in the morning, five minutes at lunch, and five minutes before bed. You want to shift your energy levels and mood, and in order to do that, you must be engaged in your topic for a continuous block of time.

## REFLECTIONS & OBSERVATIONS:

### DAY 1:

Make a list of all of the topics and hobbies that interest you. Don't overthink it. Just brainstorm. What naturally captures your interest? If nothing comes to mind, think back to a time before your illness got in the way of living your life. What did you gravitate toward back then? Let this list be your starting point.

_____

_____

_____

_____

_____

_____

_____

### DAY 40:

How did you spend your 15 minutes a day? Did you find books, blogs, and podcasts that enlightened you? Was this Booster an effective tool for sparking inspiration and motivation?

_____

_____

_____

_____

_____

_____

_____

*Chapter 6*

# CUT THE CRAP

Now that you've eliminated social media and started to fill your mind with inspiration and creativity, it's time to move on to the next mood-boosting topic: cleaning up your diet. If you already feel yourself getting defensive and have a list of reasons why you can't get in the kitchen to cook—STOP!

I know you are at the very beginning of your journey to thrive. I haven't forgotten. I've been there, and I know firsthand that shopping, prepping, and cooking meals when you feel lousy is unrealistic.

Healthy food preparation takes energy and a good spirit. If you're lacking both, you're not going to start a new diet plan. Because I know this so well, I will not ask you to commit to a specific diet in the first 40-days of the program.

Instead, I will ask you to make a few small changes to your diet that will have a big impact on how you feel.

In my own life, diet has been the single most important factor in determining how I feel. The right diet has increased my energy levels, reduced inflammation in my body, and boosted my mood. The quality of my sleep each night has improved, and my temperament has become steady and consistent. No more midafternoon slumps or erratic mood swings. I want you to also experience all of the benefits of improving your diet.

Food is powerful, which is why I discuss it here in the Boosters section of the book as well as in the Builders section of the program.

In discussing diet as a Booster, the primary goal is to create a brighter outlook. As such, the plan is simple and doable so that you can start feeling a little better each day. I will not bombard you will meal plans, recipes, calorie restriction, or expectations to shop for esoteric ingredients.

During the first 40 days, let's improve your mood and energy levels by changing your diet through elimination.

## Booster #3: Eliminate highly processed foods and foods with added sugars.

To put it simply: Cut the crap.

Stop eating processed foods with long lists of ingredients that have been treated in some way to increase shelf life or to chemically change the color or flavor of the food. The less a factory does with your food, the better.

I specify *highly* processed foods because not all processed foods are bad. Sure, it would be great if everything that we put into our mouths was grown naturally and harvested from the earth, but that's not a realistic goal when you are feeling beaten down, mentally drained, and possibly in pain.

There are plenty of items in the grocery store that are processed in some way but are still excellent, convenient additions to our diets. Nut butters, hummus, canned beans, boxed organic broths, and frozen fruits and vegetables are some examples.

My goal isn't to remove convenient food options from your life. I just want to make you more mindful of your food choices by reading labels and limiting your grocery store purchases to simply prepared foods without artificial colors, flavors, preservatives, or sweeteners.

## HOW TO STAY ON TRACK

To avoid highly processed foods, stick with foods that have very short ingredient lists—maybe three or four ingredients in all. If you're unsure if an item is heavily processed, ask yourself if you could have made the item in your own house. If not, you're probably looking at a highly processed food

Get rid of shelf-stable cookies, crackers, loaves of bread, and muffins.

Eliminate refined-grain products like white flour pasta and cereal bars.

Don't buy processed meat like deli cold cuts and hot dogs.

Stay away from sugary drinks and canned foods that are full of added sodium, sugar, and preservatives.

Instead, fill up on nuts, seeds, fruits, vegetables, and whole grains. Make it easier on yourself and buy prewashed, pre-chopped produce if the idea of prepping vegetables seems daunting.

If possible, choose the natural, whole form of a food instead of the processed form. Choose a banana rather than banana chips, even if the chips are organic and from the health food store. Choose a bowl of freshly prepared brown rice rather than a bowl of puffed brown rice breakfast cereal.

You get the idea. Don't drive yourself crazy, but try to move the needle in the right direction.

You don't need to cook new recipes or focus on any kind of calorie restriction. Just think about what you are consuming.

## YOU'RE SWEETER WITHOUT SUGAR

During this 40-day period, the only sugar that you will consume will be the sugar that naturally occurs in the foods you eat. For example, eating a sweet potato is fine, but drizzling that sweet potato with maple syrup is not.

Skip all sweeteners—even if they are organic. Avoid maple syrup, honey, agave, molasses, brown rice syrup, and coconut sugar.

Eliminating added sugars will have the effect of reducing inflammation in your body and reducing mood swings.

Research has confirmed that sugar triggers an inflammatory response in the body that can cause muscle and joint pain. Researchers have also found a link between increased sugar intake and mood disorders. There are numerous studies on both topics that you can research online, if you want to learn more.

By the time you complete 40 days of the elimination diet, you will feel better, physically and mentally, and you will have the motivated spirit to be able to consider making bigger changes to your diet in the Builders section of the book.

## REFLECTIONS & OBSERVATIONS:

DAY 1:

What do you need to do to be successful with this Booster? Did you clean out your pantry and fridge and shop for healthy snacks and pre-chopped produce? Does this elimination diet sound manageable? What are your concerns?

_____

_____

_____

_____

_____

_____

DAY 40:

How do you feel after eliminating sugar and processed foods for 40 days? Do you notice any physical changes in your body? How are your energy levels? Is this elimination diet sustainable? If you are struggling in any way, record it here.

_____

_____

_____

_____

_____

_____

*Chapter 7*

# HIT THE MENTAL RESET BUTTON

Sometimes, you just need a quick, mental reset button. That's the idea behind this quick Booster. If you're feeling blah, there's no better way to immediately shift your mood than by changing your surroundings. Don't overthink it. Just do it.

**Booster #4: Get some fresh air every single day.**

Notice that I didn't write "Go outside every single day." And I didn't write "Go for a run every single day." The ritual is to simply get some fresh air every single day.

I have worded this very intentionally, and I specifically didn't link it to exercise or to being able to physically get outdoors because I want you to be able to do this Booster on a daily basis whether you're feeling fantastic or whether you're lying in bed. It shouldn't matter if your head hurts, your feet hurt, or your entire body is failing you.

No matter what, you should be able to have access to fresh air.

## WHEN YOU'RE FEELING BAD...

If you're not feeling well, have someone lift the shades and open all of the windows in your room for you. Get under several blankets if you feel cold, but allow the fresh air to fill the room and remove all remnants of staleness. Just this simple act of allowing the outside air to fill the space can change how you feel.

"Like a breath of fresh air" is an idiom that we use in the English language for a reason! You are literally going to make it a daily habit to get many breaths of fresh air each day.

## WHEN YOU'RE FEELING GREAT...

If today is a day that you're feeling strong, go for a walk, jog, hike, or bike ride. If you don't have a tremendous amount of energy, but you can put on your sneakers, stay close to home and just walk up and down the street several times.

I hope you feel well enough to be able to go outdoors and exercise every day, but I wanted to make this fourth ritual something that you can do, rain or shine, hot or cold, feeling bad or feeling good. Get some fresh air.

If you live in a climate where the weather is good, maybe you can make it a part of your daily ritual to sit outside while you have a cup of coffee or tea. If you want to consolidate some of the daily rituals, sit outside with your motivational books or listen to a podcast. You can do multiple Boosters at the same time.

You may be wondering what you should do if the weather is awful, if it's a rainy day, or if it's the middle of the winter and there's a foot of snow outside. The goal of this daily ritual is not to make you miserable.

Assess how you feel each day. If you're feeling good and think you can brave the weather, put on extra layers of clothing or grab an umbrella and step outside for a bit. If the weather isn't ideal, aim for at least 10 minutes of fresh air, either outside or inside near the open windows. If possible, try for 20–30 minutes a day.

Getting fresh air will clear your head, fill you with energy, and rejuvenate you. And of course, it's a bonus if you can spend some time outside while the sun is shining. One of the benefits of being in the direct sun is that sunlight triggers the body to produce Vitamin D, which keeps our bones strong and healthy. The sun also triggers a mood-boosting hormone called serotonin to be released in the brain.

If you can make this Booster a natural part of your life, it won't feel like a chore. Embrace your outdoor hobbies, like gardening, bird watching, or exercising. Eat a meal outdoors whenever possible. Walk instead of drive. Park farther from the entrance when deciding on a parking space. Or when all else fails…simply open your windows.

## REFLECTIONS & OBSERVATIONS:

DAY 1:

How can you prepare for this Booster? Is there a specific time each day that you can allot for your fresh air challenge? If you are feeling well, how do you plan on spending your time outside? If your health or the weather doesn't permit you to go out, what is your plan?

_____

_____

_____

_____

_____

DAY 40:

Describe how you feel after 40 consecutive days of getting outside? Did you use this Booster as a mental reset button? Did you notice a shift in your mood after spending time outside?

_____

_____

_____

_____

_____

*Chapter 8*

# THE PERSPECTIVE CHANGER

This next task is not a new and novel way to promote positivity. There's a reason that you can probably find it in most personal development books and courses.

It works.

It forces you to assess your circumstances and change the way you perceive them. It might be challenging at first, but it will become much easier with practice and repetition:

**Booster #5: Make a list of five things that you feel grateful for today.**

I hope you aren't rolling your eyes. If you are, I get it. When I first started making gratitude lists, it felt really hokey to me, too. I felt like I was pretending to be enlightened and holy. It seemed so…self-righteous. And I felt like I was doing it all wrong.

In my heart, I was grateful for the delicious matcha latte that I was drinking, but I felt like I should be giving thanks for more important things, like being able to live in peace rather than in a war-torn village.

I thought I should be giving thanks for clean, running water and a roof over my head rather than a pedicure or a deep tissue massage.

## YOU CAN'T DO IT WRONG

It took me a while to really internalize that this list was not for anyone else to see. It was only for me. There was no right or wrong way of doing this. The items on my list could be as insignificant or as silly as I wanted.

If I felt grateful for fuzzy socks and warm blankets, then that was the truth! The point was that I was putting energy and focus into five things each day that I truly appreciated in my life. Remember that the purpose of all these daily rituals is to help cultivate a positive mindset. I'm not asking you to do anything that's a waste of your time.

## SHIFTING YOUR PERSPECTIVE

The reason why I'm having you make a gratitude list is because there's a tendency to become jaded when you are suffering physically. It's easy to fall into the habit of complaining and talking about everything that's going wrong, rather than considering the things that are going right.

I know my own tendencies when I'm in pain. I start taking inventory of all of my failing body parts:

✓ My painful left pinky.

✓ My flaming right hip.

✓ My inflamed wrists.

✓ My dull skin.

✓ My hair loss.

✓ My declining athletic ability.

…and the list could go on and on.

We are prone to becoming Debbie Downers because we are caught up with all of the physical discomforts that come along with having a chronic illness. So, the goal of this particular exercise is to help you change your perspective by taking a moment to give thanks each day.

## MY OWN SHIFT IN PERSPECTIVE

I've been doing this for so long that I can find a drop of gratitude in most things—even my autoimmune condition. No, I'm not thankful for the pain, but I'm thankful that this illness prompted so much positive change in my life.

I am now mindful of every piece of food that I put into my body. Before my diagnosis, I wasn't eating poorly, but I definitely wasn't putting a ton of thought into my food choices. As long as I had vegetables on my plate at each meal, I thought I was doing well.

This illness has inspired me to do everything in my power to strengthen my body.

I cut sugar.

I cut processed foods.

I started loading up on greens, sea vegetables, and fermented foods.

I strengthened my gut and strengthened my immune system.

I adopted a strict macrobiotic diet. By doing so, not only did I heal from unimaginable pain, but I also eliminated a bunch of other smaller issues, like debilitating seasonal allergies that plagued me each spring for 15 years.

I've always been a fan of health and wellness, but I don't think I would have had the discipline to make such drastic changes if it weren't for the painful autoimmune attacks. Who knows what other diseases I could be avoiding altogether by adopting this new lifestyle.

I'm grateful.

## MAKING YOUR LIST

Feel free to keep your gratitude list in a physical notebook so that you can re-read all of your previous days' entries.

If you'd rather have obvious reminders of your gratitude list, write each item onto a post-it note so that you can stick your notes onto walls, books, or your refrigerator door. You will be able to quickly glance at the notes and be reminded of everything good that is in your life.

I choose to keep my gratitude list in a journaling app on my phone. Each day, I open the app, look for the current day in the calendar, and write my list there.

I happen to enjoy journaling, so I also keep track of my mental state and any physical ailments that I notice. If you enjoy journaling, too, you don't have to stop with your gratitude list. You can also keep track of your other thoughts and ideas.

"Gratitude is not only the greatest of virtues, but the parent of all others."

**-Cicero**

## THE INEVITABLE CHANGE

Once you start making your daily gratitude list, it won't be long before you notice your mood shifting and becoming a bit brighter. It's inevitable!

Instead of focusing on pain and the unfairness of your circumstances, you are training your brain to magnify the good in your life. With a heart full of thankfulness, you are setting yourself up to thrive.

## REFLECTIONS & OBSERVATIONS:

DAY 1:

Quick! List five things that you feel grateful for today. Was that difficult for you? Did it take a long time to generate your list? Do you feel self-conscious about the list in any way? If so, take a moment to think about why that might be. If creating this list was time consuming, don't worry—the process gets easier with practice.

_____

_____

_____

_____

_____

_____

_____

DAY 40:

Describe the shift in your mindset after practicing 40 days of thankfulness.

_____

_____

_____

_____

_____

_____

_____

*Chapter 9*

# SHIFT THE SPOTLIGHT

The idea behind this next Booster is similar in concept to the idea behind the daily gratitude list: While you're focused on the good, you can't be focused on the bad.

It sounds like an oversimplified method to boost your mood, but it really works. You can cultivate a thriving mindset by training your mind each day to magnify all that's positive in your life.

This next Booster will train you to recognize and acknowledge the amazing qualities of the people that you come across in your daily life. You will see that this is a great exercise to shift the spotlight off your own physical ailments and shine it on someone else. Make someone smile by paying them a genuine compliment.

You will nurture your existing relationships and build new ones by being honest, kind, and uplifting.

### Booster #6: Give three genuine compliments.

Ideally, the three compliments would be given to three different people to spread the love around a bit, but that's not the important part. If you have to give all three compliments to one person, that's fine, too.

The word "compliment" is defined as being "a polite expression of praise or admiration." Here are a few examples:

o   You are an amazing communicator.

o   You are a ray of sunshine, and I feel happier when you're around.

o   You are multitalented. Is there anything you can't do?

o   You are an inspiration.

o   You are the best cook. I look forward to all of your meals.

A compliment doesn't have to ever be about anyone's physical appearance, so don't worry if you're embarrassed or concerned about making a comment about someone's eyes, hair, clothing, or smile. Stay out of trouble. You can say plenty of complimentary, appropriate things that never make light of anyone's physical attributes.

What's most important is that the compliments that you give are genuine. Don't say it if you don't mean it. There are plenty of things that you do mean, so focus on those statements instead

---

I've learned that people will forget what you said, people will forget what you did, but people will never forget how you made them feel.

**–Maya Angelou**

---

## REDIRECTING THE SPOTLIGHT

When you're in the throes of battling a chronic illness, every day has the tendency to be self-centered—especially if you're not feeling well. I know this because I've analyzed my own thoughts while I've been in pain. These are just a few of the questions I've asked myself on a near-daily basis.

o   How can *I* feel better?

o   What should *I* be eating to improve my condition?

o   Which supplements should *I* be taking?

o   Which doctors should *I* be seeing?

o   What protocols can *I* try next?

o   What exercises should *I* be doing?

Do you see the common thread running through all of these thoughts? "I" am at the heart of each one. I'm the first to admit that self-care is very important when you're trying to heal from a condition.

But, because having chronic condition can put the focus on yourself day after day, the idea behind giving three compliments daily is to shift the spotlight onto someone else for a bit. This will be good for your soul as you watch someone's face light up after hearing your compliment.

You can practice this daily, even if you are stuck in the house all day. If you happen to not be feeling well and you're at home and you only see your caregiver, give all three compliments to that caregiver.

- o Tell your caregiver that they make the most delicious soup.

- o Tell them how much you appreciate their presence.

- o Tell them that they have the most soothing voice or the most calming effect.

Every day, you have the opportunity to pour into someone else, even if it's something small like a compliment. I know when you're not feeling well, you don't have a whole lot to give. This is one easy way to be generous.

Your words have the power to uplift and to heal. Be genuine and don't hold back. It costs you nothing and bestows the gift of happiness and confidence upon someone who might need it.

You will fill someone else's well without depleting your own. And you will feel better because of it. It's a beautiful thing.

## REFLECTIONS & OBSERVATIONS:

DAY 1:

Think about your daily routine and the people you come across in your everyday life. Make a quick list of the people that you regularly see, whether it's the mailman or the coffee barista, and jot down a few compliments that come to mind.

_____

_____

_____

_____

_____

_____

_____


DAY 40:

How did this exercise affect your daily mood and outlook on life? Did this Booster prompt you to be more social and develop new relationships?

_____

_____

_____

_____

_____

_____

_____

*Chapter 10*

# SEE IT HERE FIRST

A negative mindset often starts with a single negative thought that goes unchecked. One negative thought doesn't seem like a big deal, but once you've internalized this seemingly innocuous thought and accepted it as truth, it snowballs into a series of negative thoughts.

Negative thinking perpetuates more negative thinking. Before you even realize what's happened, you've convinced yourself that you are worthless and unproductive. You fall into the black hole of despair with all of your hopes and dreams forgotten.

I know this because I've been there.

The worst part is that these negative thoughts don't represent reality. They represent a twisted, warped view of your life through a distorted lens of negativity. None of these negative thoughts have to be reflections of your life or predictions of what's to come.

How do you escape this negative cycle of dismal thoughts?

One way is to use visualization as a tool to manifest the life of your dreams. Make it a habit to focus on your greatest aspirations, even if they feel unattainable right now. Allow your imagination to soar. Internalize the images that you see in your mind.

## Booster #7: Visualize the life that you want.

Visualization is a real technique that many top athletes, entrepreneurs, and performers all employ as part of their winning strategy. Before achieving success, they are able to see it in great detail in their mind's eye.

You can use this technique to design the life that you want for yourself. You are the CEO of your mind and body, and you want to be in the business of running the highest quality life that you can envision. How empowering and uplifting to be able to see it all happen before it actually comes to pass!

You don't need a lot of time—just a few minutes will do—but you are welcome to visualize for as long as you would like. Visualization is really like daydreaming in intense, realistic detail.

If you are not in a positive mindset when you first begin this exercise, don't stress. As with anything, it takes time for it to flow naturally. When I first started, it was difficult for me to imagine an inspiring life.

All of my goals couldn't be attained because of my physical limitations. With time, my thoughts did begin to change. I started thinking less about the goals I couldn't achieve and began focusing on what gifts I still had to offer the world. My best-life visualizations kept shifting as my mindset became more positive and inspired.

> "Everything you can imagine is real."

> **-Pablo Picasso**

## HOW TO GET STARTED

Begin by finding a quiet spot where you won't be disturbed for a few minutes. This is an exercise that you can do regardless of your current state of health.

Sit or lie down comfortably and close your eyes. Picture yourself in as much detail as you can, feeling healthy and vibrant.

See yourself moving well and feeling absolutely no pain or discomfort anywhere in your body. Imagine in as much detail as you can what you would look like in this state.

See the smile on your face.

The brightness of your skin.

The life in your eyes.

The strength of your healthy fingernails and hair.

Picture yourself resuming all of the activities that you've put on hold because of your illness.

Imagine being able to do everything that you've always desired, whether that's running a marathon or running your own business.

Imagine yourself playing with your children or your pets and being able to get up and down off the floor effortlessly.

Picture the type of food that you would be eating in this magnificent state of perfect health.

Imagine only the most nutritious choices in your kitchen and on your plate. See the food nourishing you, feeding the cells in your body, and energizing you.

Imagine yourself with so much energy that you can get back to the business of really living your life.

Take a moment to think about your goals in every part of your life, personal or professional.

Now see yourself achieving each and every goal.

## VISUALIZATION BECOMES REALITY

Earlier this year, I visualized becoming a published author. I could see myself at every stage of the process. I could see myself scribbling notes on sheets of white paper at my dining table and then typing the manuscript at my computer. I could see myself smiling as I held a printed copy of my book in my hands. I could see myself in perfect health, with no pain, attending book signing events and getting my book to the people who needed it most.

Even though it's been on my bucket list to write a book for as long as I can remember, it was only after I began visualizing it in excruciating detail that it actually came to fruition. I had to picture it in such detail that it was like seeing a video reel of my life.

When I saw myself scribbling notes, I could see the color of the pen that I was using. I could turn my head to the right and see the mug on the table filled with my favorite tea. I could turn to the left and look out the window to see my front yard, filled with flowers. Everything in my visualization had to be exact so that my mind could absorb it as an eventual reality.

When I attempted to write this book in the past, the few chapters that I attempted were abandoned in a lonely folder on my computer. My desire to become an author was not enough to make it happen.

In my mind, I reasoned that the time wasn't right. I understand now that seeing it in my mind as a reality was a huge factor in pushing to the finish line.

## WHAT IF THE VISUALIZATION IS NEVER FULLY REALIZED?

Will every detail of your visualization come to pass as you imagined it? Maybe…maybe not.

It doesn't matter.

I have no idea if I will be in perfect health as I attend book signings. I don't know if I will even have any book signings to attend!

The point is that my visualizations put me in the right frame of mind to even believe that it was possible. I felt a wave of positivity lifting me to my destination of becoming a published author. Daily visualization gave me the motivation to achieve my dream of publishing a book to help others.

I encourage you to visualize your wildest dreams in vivid detail. See it exactly as you want it to happen, and then see it again tomorrow, the next day, and the day after that.

Keep seeing it in your mind's eye until you are completely convinced that your visualization of being healthy and accomplishing your dreams can become your reality.

## REFLECTIONS & OBSERVATIONS:

### DAY 1:

Before you sit down to practice your first visualization, write about the exact life you want. Describe your personal and professional goals as well as your health aspirations. Include any dreams that you've put on hold as a result of your chronic illness. Decide whether these are goals that you'd still like to attain.

_____

_____

_____

_____

_____

_____

_____

### DAY 40:

How do you feel after practicing 40 days of visualization? Are you able to see your desired path in excruciating detail? How has your visualization changed since Day One? Are you feeling inspired?

_____

_____

_____

_____

_____

_____

_____

*Chapter 11*

# PREPARE FOR A BRIGHTER TOMORROW

This is it—your eighth and final Booster—and it's all about sleep.

Did you know that lack of sleep has been linked to increased rates of depression and anxiety?

A sleep study conducted by University of Pennsylvania researchers found that subjects who were limited to less than five hours of sleep a night for one week experienced more tension, mental exhaustion, and mood disturbances. Call me crazy, but the last thing you need is more tension, mental exhaustion, and mood disturbances.

The whole purpose of completing 40 days of Boosters is to improve your outlook and increase your zest for life. You don't want to counteract all of your mood-boosting work by skimping on sleep.

By developing good sleep habits, you will give yourself the healthiest baseline for a positive mindset and a good-natured temperament. Your final mood-boosting task brings you to the end of your day with the promise of a brighter tomorrow.

**Booster #8: Get a good night of sleep.**

I don't know about you, but living with a chronic illness has made my sleep habits very erratic. I've experienced days when I've been so exhausted that I've crashed for 16 hours straight. I've also been on the other end of the spectrum where my energy is boundless, and I have stayed up way past my bedtime. (I justified these late nights by saying that I was making up for lost time.)

In order to get a consistent amount of sleep, I've had to become very intentional about creating a bedtime routine and sticking to it. I know I feel so much better when I'm getting good sleep each night, but I have a hard time climbing into bed when the time comes. This Booster continues to be a work in progress for me.

As you read through this final chapter of the 40-day program, just remind yourself that it's OK to be a work in progress. You aren't stuck. You haven't failed if you miss a day. You can get right back on track and continue on.

Every day, you have the opportunity to adjust your sails and change direction. You have the power to make small changes that will result in big shifts in your life.

## WHY SLEEP IS SO IMPORTANT

Sleep is very important for the body, especially if you have a chronic condition that causes pain. Healing occurs while you sleep, as your body repairs cells and releases proteins that are necessary for healthy immune system response. Without a good night of sleep, you are denying your body the opportunity to go through the housekeeping processes that it needs to stay in tip-top shape.

Besides the rest and healing, it's essential for you to get a good night of sleep so that you can be in the best state of mind the next day. The probability of thriving increases if you are well rested.

Your other Boosters become more effective, and you have the emotional resources to handle the ups and downs of your day. You'll notice that everything feels a bit more manageable when you've had a good night of sleep.

It is exhausting to have a constant battle raging inside of you, so be sure to give your body the rest and repair that it needs each night. Incorporate this Booster into your daily routine immediately and try to be disciplined about sticking to it.

## SETTING YOUR BEDTIME

In theory, I know that a good night of sleep sounds wonderful. Most people would love to benefit from more sleep and higher quality sleep. But, to actually experience it, you must be very intentional with your time.

Begin by establishing a consistent sleep schedule where you go to bed at the same time each night and wake up at the same time each morning. Everyone is different, but most people need between seven and nine hours of sleep per night to function optimally during the day.

Chances are, if you're like most busy people I know, you're not in that target range. You probably have good intentions of getting into bed at a reasonable hour each night, but your good intentions keep getting derailed.

If you know this is going to be a challenging process for you to increase the number of hours that you sleep, don't get extreme. Start out by getting into bed a half hour earlier than usual. A half hour earlier isn't necessarily the end goal, but it's a small step in the right direction. The idea is that you will shift your entire sleep schedule and fall asleep a half hour earlier just by being in the bed sooner.

If all goes well and you can maintain that routine for one week, move the clock back another half hour. Keep adding an extra half hour to your total sleep schedule until you hit your optimal amount of sleep.

Even though you won't spend all 40 days of the program getting your optimal amount of sleep, that's OK. Each week will be an improvement over the previous week.

Just keep in mind that the number of hours that you spend in bed does not equal the number of hours of sleep you get. Being in bed for seven hours isn't the same thing as being asleep for seven hours.

If your target is seven hours of sleep and you need to be up at 6:00 a.m., I would recommend getting into bed no later than 10:30 p.m. so you have a chance of being asleep by the time the clock strikes 11:00 p.m.

Once you determine your sleep schedule, build a relaxing routine leading up to your bedtime.

## DEVELOP A BEDTIME ROUTINE

A relaxing bedtime routine signals to your body and mind that it's time to start winding down. It doesn't have to be a long process, and you can even change it depending on the season.

In colder weather, my bedtime routine includes a warm bath. In warmer weather, I skip the soak altogether. Regardless of the season, I have a book on my bedside table that I read each night and a cup of herbal tea to sip in bed.

What sounds relaxing and sleep inducing to you? Soft music? Gentle yoga stretches? A warm beverage? Take a moment to think about what your own routine should look like.

---

> "There is a time for many words, and there is also a time for sleep."
>
> **-Homer**

---

## TIPS FOR BETTER SLEEP

Here are some additional tips to help you develop healthy sleep habits:

o   If you drink caffeinated beverages like coffee or tea throughout the day, try getting it all in before noon. You may be more sensitive to caffeine than you realize. Even if you are able to fall asleep with little trouble, the caffeine in your system could still disrupt your sleep by waking you throughout the night. It's better to be on the safe side and cut off your caffeine consumption at noon every day. If you suffer from an afternoon lull and need a caffeine boost, find other ways to get energized. Maybe this is the time of day to practice Booster #4 and get some fresh air.

o   Set your thermostat to 60–67 degrees in your bedroom. Experts say that this temperature range is ideal for sleeping. Our internal body temperature naturally fluctuates throughout the day, peaks in the late afternoon, and then drops as our bodies get ready for sleep. Keeping your bedroom cool facilitates this natural cooling process within the body and helps you stay asleep throughout the night.

o   Eliminate sources of light from your bedroom. Light is one of the most important factors regulating our circadian rhythm. Too much light at night could suppress the body's release of melatonin, the hormone that sends signals to our bodies to get tired and fall asleep. Use room-darkening shades to block light from lamp posts, cars, and buildings outside. Cover digital displays on alarm clocks, cable boxes, other types of electronics, and home security systems.

o   Enforce an electronic shut down for a solid hour before getting into bed. That means no phones, no computers, and no televisions. Electronics emit large amounts of blue-wavelength light, which can disrupt the body's circadian rhythm. During the day, blue light is helpful in keeping you awake and alert, but in the evening, it has the effect of suppressing melatonin production and keeping you awake.

o   Invest in a comfortable pillow, mattress, and bedding set. Not only is it important for a good night's sleep, but it's also important if you have a bad flare-up of your illness and find yourself in bed for a period of time and your bed becomes your dining table, home office, and couch.

o   Stop eating two to three hours before bedtime. Begin training your body to understand that it's time to begin the daily shutdown, and it's not time to eat, but time to rest. It's a good idea to make sure your food has been digested and has moved out of the stomach before you lie down for the night. This will reduce the possibility of heartburn and ensure a restful night of sleep.

## DEALING WITH INSOMNIA

If you have your relaxing bedtime routine in place but struggle with insomnia, I recommend listening to a form of guided meditation called yoga nidra. Chances are, you'll drift off to sleep while listening in bed with your eyes closed.

You can find free recordings online, and you may find them very helpful if you need help slowing down your racing thoughts. There was a time when I used yoga nidra to fall asleep every night for many months because it was the only reliable method to quiet my mind.

Without yoga nidra, my mind chatter was incessant. I would stop thinking of one thing, only to find that my thoughts were wandering to new topics and concerns. If this sounds familiar, give yoga nidra a try. You have nothing to lose. If you are interested in learning more about this meditation practice, we will revisit this topic in Chapter 14.

## QUICK-TO-SLEEP COUNTING EXERCISE

My other suggestion to help you fall asleep is similar to the concept of counting sheep. My yoga teacher taught me this counting backwards technique, which is often found within yoga nidra meditations.

If you don't have a yoga nidra recording on hand, or if you don't need something quite so extensive, try this shorter exercise where you count each of your inhales and exhales as you breathe:

Lie down in bed with your eyes closed, and notice the movement of your belly as you breathe. With each inhale, notice that your belly expands, and with each exhale, your belly falls toward your spine. Now count each inhale and exhale in your mind, beginning with the number 54 and making your way down to the number one.

You'll count like this: 54 belly up, 54 belly down. 53 belly up, 53 belly down, 52 belly up, 52 belly down, etc. If you lose your place while counting, go back to 54 and start over. This is a surprisingly effective method to induce sleepiness. Try it and see what you think.

## REFLECTIONS & OBSERVATIONS:

DAY 1:

Plan your evening routine here. How many hours of sleep will you aim to get? What time do you need to get into bed in order to hit your target? What will you include in your bedtime routine? Music? Reading? Journaling?

_____

_____

_____

_____

_____

_____

DAY 40:

How has the quantity and quality of your sleep improved since Day One? Do you notice a difference in your disposition and outlook? How has your bedtime routine changed over the course of 40 days?

_____

_____

_____

_____

_____

_____

# BOOSTERS CHEAT SHEET

Incorporate these eight Boosters into your routine for 40 consecutive days. These daily habits will transform your mindset and spark the drive within you to live a fulfilled, inspired life. Get prepared to thrive.

1. Commit to a social media fast.

2. Spend at least 15 minutes a day immersing yourself in a podcast, blog, or book on any topic that inspires you.

3. Eliminate highly processed foods and foods with added sugars.

4. Get some fresh air every single day.

5. Make a list of five things that you feel grateful for today.

6. Give three genuine compliments.

7. Visualize the life that you want.

8. Get a good night of sleep.

*Section Two*

# BUILDERS

# Chapter 12

# SUSTAINABLE MOVEMENT

Congratulations!

You've completed the first 40 days of the program! You've incorporated all eight Boosters into your life and turned them into daily habits. Take a moment to feel proud.

Developing a new routine takes work, and not everyone is willing to do the work. It's easier to do nothing. Your daily commitment to the program and faith in the process carried you through. You did it.

My hope is that you can sense the shift in your disposition and outlook. You should feel lighter and brighter and ready to take on more. If you're not quite there, that's OK. Stick with the original Boosters for another ten days before beginning this section. See how you feel.

I want you to feel hopeful and excited about the future. The thought of taking on more to enhance your life and live in better health should not overwhelm you. You should feel prepared to tap into the positive momentum you generated over the past 40 days.

When you are ready to move on to this next phase of the program, do not give up on your Boosters. These Boosters are now a permanent part of your life.

I know I mentioned the possibility of returning to social media after 40 days, but if you would like to maintain your laser focus, I highly recommend continuing your fast. It's much easier to figure out where your new life will lead you if you eliminate unnecessary background noise.

It's now time to add Builders to your routine. These are the healthy lifestyle habits that are the foundation for your new, inspired life. I've listed the Builders in no particular order. Feel free to read through them all and then decide which to try first.

Remember that Builders aren't necessarily daily habits. Some can be incorporated into your life on a daily basis, but you will quickly see that many of the Builders are meant to be done less frequently.

Try one new Builder at a time. Spend one week getting used to the new addition to your routine, and then move on to add another Builder.

If for some reason, something on this list doesn't work for you, don't stress about it. These eight Builders are just the suggested building blocks upon which you will grow your own personal goals and dreams. The first Builder is all about movement.

## Builder #1: Move your body in a pain-free zone.

I can't write about healthy lifestyle habits without including a discussion about physical movement.

If you are reading this section before completing the first 40-days of the program because you like reading ahead (like me), any kind of physical movement may sound overwhelming and unrealistic. If this is the case, just trust the process for now and believe that when you return to this section in 40 days, you will feel differently.

In my own experience, I've found that when I'm feeling hopeful and inspired, the energy and desire to move is a natural byproduct of that inspiration. Yes, physical pain is real, and I'm not saying this is a simple game of mind over matter.

I'm saying that after 40 days, the momentum and trajectory of your life will be an upward powerful force. Even if your body isn't 100 percent pain free, you will not dread the thought of moving. It will actually sound appealing and energizing.

## RETHINKING THE CONCEPT OF EXERCISE

In this section, I'm asking you to move your body in some way that makes you feel good. I'm almost reluctant to use the word "exercise" because exercise conjures such strong images for many people.

Heart pumping.

Pavement pounding.

Heavy lifting.

Grunting.

Sweating.

Pushing hard.

Depending on your chronic condition, these words may be exhausting or even discouraging to read. All exercise isn't like this, but it's often what comes to mind when we think of words like exercise or fitness.

So today, I propose a shift in your thinking. Stop thinking about traditional "exercise" and start thinking of simply moving your body. There are so many ways to move your body: dancing, stretching, walking, bike riding, gardening, yoga, swimming, lifting weights, cardio drumming, hiking, pilates, etc.

## GETTING STARTED

If it's been a long time since you've exerted yourself physically, start out slow. Just get into the habit of moving, stretching, and feeling energized on a regular basis. Don't even worry about working up a sweat.

For now, just practice moving in a pain-free zone. Your joints and bones shouldn't hurt, and you shouldn't feel any sharpness in your muscles, tendons or ligaments. If you feel pain, modify your movement.

If you feel good after a few days, feel free to increase the intensity. Just remember that it shouldn't hurt. If your knees are already screaming at you, don't aggravate them further by signing up for a trampoline class with your friends.

You must honor your body and realize that because you're dealing with a chronic illness, it's possible that you might not be able to do on Wednesday what you were able to do on Monday.

Don't compare or use any kind of metrics to assess your progress. Just use your body as a gauge to know when you should stop and when you should go; when you should push, and when you should lay off. We want movement to become a permanent part of your life. Let's aim for sustainability.

## FUN = SUSTAINABILITY

I want you to move your body because it feels good. If you don't know what feels good, try experimenting until you figure it out.

Start with an activity. Does it feel good? If so, keep going. If not, stop and do something else. Walk until it isn't fun. When walking isn't fun anymore, grab a jump rope. When jumping rope isn't fun, ride a bike. When biking isn't fun, go stretch, dance, or lift weights.

Make sense?

Do something, and only do it for as long as you perceive it to be pain free and fun. The second it stops being fun, it stops being sustainable. Practice moving in a way that can become a natural and consistent part of your life.

For now, don't worry about the duration of your activity. Stop after 10 minutes if you'd like. If it's fun, you will come back tomorrow for more. The length of time you spend on movement will naturally increase. I am hopeful for the day that you move for 30 minutes without even noticing the passage of time!

## HOW I MOVE

I happen to love walking outside in the fresh air, lifting weights at home or in the gym, and yoga—either in my bedroom or at a studio.

Yoga is a wonderful form of movement because it serves the dual purpose of moving your body and quieting your mind. It really is a moving meditation! These days, most of my yoga happens on my bedroom floor because it's so convenient, but the studio experience is wonderful, and you may prefer it.

If you are new to yoga or if you practice a type of yoga that requires a heated room or equipment like blocks, bolsters, blankets, and straps, you should look for a local studio where you can attend classes.

If you can get yourself to a studio that teaches yin yoga or a Bikram-inspired yoga, I highly recommend both types of yoga for different reasons. These styles are quite different from one another, but both are very therapeutic in their own way.

## A PREDICTABLE YOGA PRACTICE

A Bikram-inspired yoga class is a set sequence of postures performed in a hot room. Studios may vary the temperature and humidity levels, but I recommend finding a 95-degree room. Many studios run the heat over 105 degrees. You may enjoy it, but I find that even a few degrees cooler makes the experience more enjoyable.

A true Bikram class is taught under strict guidelines and temperature. I specify a "Bikram-inspired" yoga class so that you can shop around for a studio that teaches the set sequence in a cooler room.

You should look for a hot yoga studio that has taken a few liberties with the original Bikram practice in order to serve their students. A slightly cooler room is one liberty that I appreciate!

## WHY IS IT SO GREAT?

Once you get past the initial shock of walking into a hot, humid room to exercise, you'll notice that the heat and humidity feel great on the muscles and joints.

Also, unlike other types of hot yoga classes that include an active flow component, a Bikram-inspired class tends to be fairly stationary, so you're not raising your heart rate by moving around the mat.

There are no weight-bearing poses on the hands in this series of postures, which is great news for anyone dealing with shoulder, elbow, wrist, or hand pain. No downward facing dogs or planks!

It's also nice to know that the poses that you practice in your first class will be the same as the poses you practice in your second class, tenth class, and hundredth class. That's a real bonus when you have painful flare-ups and never know what body part will be aching.

If you know the sequence, you can plan a modification for yourself or opt out of a particular pose. There's no anxiety caused by wondering what's coming next and whether or not you'll be able to do it. Predictability in yoga is essential when you are managing an unpredictable condition that affects your physical body.

## SLOW AND STEADY WITH YIN YOGA

The other style of yoga that I love and that you might enjoy, too, is called yin yoga. It's a very slow-paced class where you hold each pose for several minutes in order to access deep layers of fascia, the connective tissue in your body. By holding each pose for an extended length of time, you stimulate the energy flow through the body's meridians.

In traditional Chinese medicine, life energy or "qi" flows through the meridians, which are thought to be energy pathways. The idea is to remove energy blockages with these extended holds and get the qi flowing freely through the body. This style of yoga really feels like a gateway to meditation because you become so still during the extended hold times that your mind naturally begins to relax.

I highly recommend this form of yoga, especially on days when you don't have the energy for much movement. It feels quite therapeutic, and I bet you will feel much better after just a few poses.

Once you learn some of the commonly practiced yin poses, you can use your own blocks and pillows and practice at home, in bed, or on the floor of your bedroom like me.

## HOW TO CREATE YOUR OWN YOGA FLOW CLASS

This next section is for those of you who have an existing yoga practice and basic knowledge of poses and transitions. If that's not you, feel free to move on to the next chapter.

If you are still reading, I want to provide you with the basic framework for structuring your own flow class.

If you're not prone to painful flare-ups in your hands, elbows, and shoulders, a flow class might be your favorite style of yoga to practice. You can build strength with poses like chaturanga dandasana (a yoga push-up), work your core muscles in plank pose, and get a great stretch in downward facing dog or dolphin.

As long as you're comfortable on your hands, vinyasa flow can be a strong, but meditative, practice.

It's not too difficult to structure your own short class, and it gives you an option of staying home on days when you're a bit lower on energy and would rather practice on your own. This is how I would recommend structuring a basic 30-minute flow:

0–5 minutes

Close your eyes, shut out the world, and begin to focus on your breath. Set an intention for your practice. Your intention doesn't have to be particularly profound, but you certainly can go ahead and think about your purpose in life or your purpose for getting on your mat.

Instead of an intention, you can state a few positive affirmations to uplift your spirit. For example: I am strong; I am healthy; I am enough.

When you are ready, slowly open your eyes and spend a few minutes doing some light stretching. I like to reach my arms overhead and stretch the sides of my body. I also do some gentle seated twists, and maybe some neck rolls, wrist stretches, and shoulder stretches.

5–10 minutes

I always include a few rounds of sun salutations at the start of my practice. During this time, I warm up my body and I also manage to completely clear my mind by focusing on each inhale and exhale that accompanies every pose. The best thing about sun salutations is that they are so engrained into my memory that I can simply move without thinking.

If you are not yet at the point where sun salutations flow naturally without much thought, don't worry. Look online for a video of sun salutation A, B, or C. Watch all three and see if you have a preference.

If you include the same sun salutation sequence at the beginning of every flow, you will learn it very quickly. Don't forget that you are at home, so you can modify anything you'd like without feeling self-conscious. When my hands and wrists are acting up, I skip all the down dogs, planks, and chaturangas. Your yoga practice shouldn't create any stress. It should be a relaxing and centering experience.

<u>10–20 minutes</u>

Now that your warm-up has ended, it's time to move into the heart of your practice. Think about how long you'd like to hold each pose. This is up to you, and you can move as quickly or as slowly as you like, but my preference is to hold poses for about 30 seconds, or five full breaths. I assume that each full breath is about six seconds long (i.e., three seconds for your inhale; three seconds for your exhale).

Following this simple math, a sequence that includes ten postures will take you about five minutes to complete. And of course, if you are practicing the right and left sides of your body, your five-minute sequence will actually be a ten-minute practice.

The poses to include in this section are up to you, but typically, I practice strong standing postures like Warrior 1, Warrior 2, side angle pose, triangle pose, wide-legged forward bend, and goddess pose.

<u>20–30 minutes</u>

At this point, assess how you feel. Some days, you might feel very energized and want to stay on your feet. If that's the case, go ahead and repeat your ten-minute flow. Other days, you might want to do some floor work and stretch a specific body part. Go ahead and take a seat. Work on whatever body part is calling for attention.

When your hips feel tight, sit for a few minutes in various pigeon pose variations. When your shoulders and chest feel tight, lie down across a yoga block or practice other heart openers. The beauty of your at-home practice is that you can do whatever you want. Experiment, play, and enjoy yourself.

If all else fails and you can't get to a studio or figure out how to structure your own class, turn to the internet. YouTube is your friend, and I'm positive that you will be able to find a good yoga class if you search for one.

## REFLECTIONS & OBSERVATIONS:

<u>DAY 1:</u>

Take a moment to list the ways that you've enjoyed moving your body in the past. How do you feel about incorporating consistent movement into your life? Are you nervous? Excited? When will you fit this into your day? How can you make this a sustainable habit?

_____

_____

_____

_____

_____

_____

_____

<u>One Week Check-In:</u>

How did your first week of movement feel? Did you have fun? Was it sustainable? Are you planning to keep this Builder in your life? If so, what other types of activities do you want to try? Will you attempt a new Builder this week?

_____

_____

_____

_____

_____

_____

_____

## Chapter 13

# AFTER CUTTING THE CRAP

Forty days ago, you made the conscious decision to eliminate processed foods and sugar from your diet. Even though it wasn't a complete diet plan that included recipes and shopping lists, it was a first step in the right direction.

The elimination diet was intended to be easy in the sense that it didn't require you to shop or cook any specific meals.

Meal plans require energy, and 40 days ago, your energy levels and enthusiasm were lower than what they are today. You are now ready to build upon your elimination plan and intentionally start a diet that is specific for your condition.

**Builder #2: Pick a diet to follow that promises to heal your body.**

Hopefully, you are already experiencing some of the benefits of cleaning up your diet. Have you noticed a difference in your skin? The quality of your sleep? Your mood? Your energy levels? Have you noticed any change in the frequency or severity of your symptoms?

In this next phase of the program, get ready for a more dramatic shift across the board. You will continue to improve your mood and feel better physically once you begin following a specific diet filled with nutrient-dense foods.

## FOOD IS POWERFUL

I know that many of you have been led to believe that your chronic condition is permanent in every way—the severity of symptoms, the frequency of the symptoms, and even in the lifelong nature of the illness. It's depressing when doctors leave no hope for improvement.

Let me assure you that there are people healing from "incurable" diseases every day. I know because I've met them and heard their stories. These people were given no hope by the medical community, so they were left no option but to find hope in alternative healing.

They overhauled their diets, committed to strict eating plans, and their illnesses retreated and disappeared. End-stage cancers; gone. Necrotic bones; healed. Chronic symptoms; vanished.

For some reason, Western medicine is reluctant to attribute such healing power to diet. These miraculous stories of healing are brushed off and explained away.

What these stories do for me is give me tremendous hope. I've learned that you have more control over your condition than you are led to believe. Even if you don't experience a full-on cure, you can improve tremendously with diet.

## FIND A DIET

Do some research to find the most recommended diets for your medical condition. Spend a few hours at the library or the bookstore flipping through books about cooking, eating, and healing from inflammatory conditions.

Visit online forums, read testimonials and reviews from people who have followed specific diets, and ask your doctor if there is a particular diet for healing from your condition or reducing the severity of symptoms.

I'm not going to discuss the merits of any specific diet in this section because that's beyond the scope of this book. This book was never intended to be a "how-to-heal manual." It was always intended to be a "how-to-thrive" manual, and you don't need to be cured of your illness to thrive.

Although I am partial to my own individualized eating plan to manage my condition, I believe strongly that **there is more than one path that can lead to healing**. Do your own research and determine what diet is right for you.

Even though I'm not recommending any specific diets here, I will discuss why it's so important for you to pick a diet plan and stick to it.

First, let's discuss the word "diet."

The word "diet" has unfortunately become synonymous with the phrase "weight loss plan." That is not what I mean when I use the word diet. I'm not talking about quantity of food or caloric value of food. I am simply referring to the collection of food that makes it down your gullet.

Choosing a diet is important because it affects your mindset. Beyond the physical effects of improving digestion, skin, hair, mood, sleep quality, and pain levels, it creates a sense of hope!

You truly begin to believe that you can feel better than you do now, and you start to feel inspired by the belief that you have a bit of control where you thought you had none.

## CONTROL WHAT YOU CAN, DON'T WORRY ABOUT WHAT YOU CAN'T

You don't have a lot of control over what hand you're dealt in life. You have been diagnosed with a chronic illness. That's the reality. What you do have control over is the fuel that you put into your body. You have complete control over every single morsel of food that you put into your mouth.

Even if you don't feel sensitive to food choices, I assure you that each food that you consume produces a different effect in your body—from the insulin released by your cells, to the acid produced by your stomach, to the inflammatory response, as measured by certain biomarkers. There are real biological processes that are affected by what you consume.

Trust that the right diet can make a big difference in how you feel. Be open to different possibilities. If there are principles of more than one diet that work for you, go ahead and combine what you've learned into a unique diet plan that's optimal for your body.

At this point in my life, I've combined various diets and philosophies into a single plan that works well for me. If you are diligent and open-minded with your research efforts, I am confident that you will be successful in figuring out what kind of diet is best for you.

## COMMIT TO FOUR MONTHS

If you are starting from scratch, begin by committing to a single diet for four straight months. Is that an arbitrary time frame? Maybe. Four months is the length of time that I spent on my first strict autoimmune diet.

I discovered that by the time I hit the four-month mark, I no longer felt like I was struggling with food choices. My new style of eating morphed into a way of life. I stopped having cravings for unhealthy foods and I didn't feel deprived in any way.

During that four-month period, I kept a daily journal to keep track of how I felt. I recorded details about pain, improvements in my body, and my mental state. I highly recommend that you keep track of your own daily physical and mental status so that you can assess the effectiveness of your diet over time. See how you feel after four months and continue experimenting.

If a particular diet doesn't work and you don't feel much better after four months, don't let the outcome upset you. Get inspired and find something new. Stay motivated by your discipline. Stay motivated by your journey.

I like to envision myself as a detective in search of the secret to my own personal wellness. If something doesn't work well or if you hit a dead end, just change directions. Every person's body is a little different, so the formula that works for your friend with the same condition might not be the same formula that works for you.

Don't get too tied to what you think "should" be. It is what it is, even if it doesn't make sense or seem fair. Keep tweaking, experimenting, and using your intuition, and you'll create the diet that works best for you.

## STAYING ON TRACK

One common obstacle that prevents people from sticking to their diet is that special diets can feel very isolating. It's difficult to be a dinner guest in anyone's home, and it's tough to attend parties where other people are providing the food.

Eating in our culture is a very social experience, and when you are unable to eat what everyone else is eating, it can make you feel left out.

I find it very useful to have two or three go-to recipes that I can make in large quantities and bring to events at other people's houses. I love that I can share a small part of my life with others and maybe even introduce them to a nutritious and delicious dish that they might otherwise never try.

I used to get stressed about making food that people might dislike, but I'm not bothered by that anymore. If people don't enjoy the food, that's OK. My food still generates lots of conversation, and that's a great opportunity to be social and share my experience.

## REALITY CHECK

I know this is a sobering thought, but it's a reality check that you might need. Being on a strict diet to manage your chronic condition can feel isolating at times, but it is far more isolating to be confined to your bed because you feel awful.

If you can actually find a diet that makes you feel better, then stick to it. Put it on your daily gratitude list. Give thanks. Don't worry about what everyone else is eating. Attend all the parties you want and bring your own food from home. You have the discipline to do this!

## EATING AT RESTAURANTS

If you are going to a restaurant, don't be embarrassed to bring your own food from home. I always make it a point to order a drink or side dish of vegetables so that I'm a paying customer.

If everyone at the table is curious about why you brought your own food, or if the restaurant staff questions you, just say that you are on a strict medical diet. That's usually enough information to get people to leave you alone.

They don't want to pry and potentially cause an emotional scene, so telling them that you are on a strict medical diet is usually enough for everyone to be accommodating.

Before you go out, look online and review the restaurant menu. It's possible that there will be numerous options that fit your diet. It's also a good idea to try to think of a go-to meal that you know you can order at most restaurants.

Don't forget that you can always ask to speak to the chef. I've found that the cooks are often willing to make you something that's not even on the menu if you talk to them about your food restrictions. People are quite compassionate by nature, so allow them to help you find a solution when you are out.

Look—I know that nothing about this is ideal, but it's worth the effort. Take the time to put a healing diet in place and see if you can make a difference. You have nothing to lose, and chances are, you will feel better.

## REFLECTIONS & OBSERVATIONS:

DAY 1:

What hopes do you have for your life as you begin the search for a healing diet? Do you believe that it's possible to improve your mental state and your pain levels with the food that you consume? Are you concerned about making a four-month commitment?

_____

_____

_____

_____

_____

_____

One Week Check-In:

What have you accomplished in the past week? Did you talk to your doctor, research the options, and choose a healing diet plan? Have you started cooking and eating for your condition? If so, how do you feel physically and emotionally? Are you prepared to add another Builder into your life at this time? Remember, there's no rush!

_____

_____

_____

_____

_____

_____

# Chapter 14

# REDUCE STRESS NATURALLY

If you're ready for some magic, you've turned to the right chapter. Life is never quite the same after you begin a consistent meditation practice. In the Boosters section of the program, I briefly mentioned trying a particular form of meditation (yoga nidra) to combat insomnia.

Whether you struggle with insomnia or sleep like a baby, meditation is a worthwhile skill to learn. I call it a skill because it actually gets easier the more you do it.

You can read about the benefits of meditation all day and agree with the research that demonstrates its effectiveness as a stress-relieving and pain-relieving tool, but nothing replaces the act of actually sitting down and doing it.

**Builder #3: Develop a regular meditation practice to manage stress.**

Begin with two sessions a week and see how you feel. Feel free to experiment with different types of meditation to see what's right for you. You can find guided meditations online, local meditation classes at yoga studios, or several different meditation apps that are downloadable on your phone.

In the beginning, you might try meditating and think it's not for you. Some days, you will easily enter the zone, and other days, you will be making grocery lists in your head and thinking about the dry cleaning that you need to drop off.

Don't give up, and don't get discouraged. It's an evolving practice. Everyone who is new to meditation is going through the same thing.

When I first decided to develop a meditation practice, I experimented a ton. One day, I meditated while practicing a forceful breathing technique. The next day, I tried breathing normally while focusing on my third eye. Then, I tried using music in the background. One time, I tried to meditate with my eyes open. Each time I tried a new technique, I learned what worked and what didn't.

Don't be afraid of trying something new. There isn't a one-size-fits-all approach to meditation. You'll find what works for you, and once you do, you'll begin to benefit from the incredible powers of meditation—the power to reduce stress, promote deeper sleep, and even cure physical ailments and lessen physical pain.

I am most interested in introducing you to meditation as an effective way to manage stress because it's a real factor that can affect how you feel physically. This is a big deal when you have chronic illness that causes physical pain in your body. As a yoga and meditation teacher, I've always believed in a mind-body connection, but I'm not sure if I really understood it to the extent that I do now.

Stress, which most people think of as just being a mental struggle, can ooze right out of your mind and into your joints and tissues. As surprising as it may be, and as reluctant as people are to admit the connection, stress causes a biological response. The adrenal glands manufacture and release stress hormones like dopamine, adrenaline, norepinephrine, cortisol, and prolactin during a stress response, and all of these substances impact the body.

While these hormones are necessary and helpful in a true fight-or-flight scenario where you're trying to outrun a lion, most of us are not being chased by wild animals in our day-to-day life. Managing stress with meditation is an accessible solution to deal with everyday worries.

## HOW STRESS TRIGGERED MY ILLNESS

For years, I managed my autoimmune condition with a strict macrobiotic diet. It kept painful flare ups to a minimum and, for the most part, I had a completely normal, healthy life.

That all changed when I lived through the stress of my eight-year-old daughter's kidney transplant. It wasn't an unexpected surgery because I'd been anticipating a transplant since her birth, but that didn't make the experience any easier or any less stressful.

I am convinced that my body absorbed the tremendous stress of this surgery and triggered a series of autoimmune attacks. Out of the blue, my right knee became red, swollen, and so painful that I could barely walk. I also developed pain in my left hand that was so severe that I couldn't even make a fist. My macrobiotic diet had no relieving effect on any of this terrible pain.

In the months that followed my daughter's transplant, I experienced more pain in different areas of my body as the medical complications in my daughter's condition continued to pour in.

Acute organ rejection, steroid-induced diabetes, and an aggressive kidney virus were a few of the very stressful challenges my daughter experienced. My body responded to this stress by increasing the severity of painful flare-ups during this period.

It was only after being home from the hospital with the very acute medical stress gone that my knee started to improve and my hands started to feel better. It was this experience that led me to understand that stress can absolutely trigger physical pain. If I had any doubts about a mind-body connection before, they were gone now.

You would think that as a yoga and meditation teacher, I would be able to effectively combat stress, but it's easier said than done. When it's your own child whose life is at risk, it's very difficult to roll out your yoga mat and practice yoga (especially if you're in a hospital). It's very difficult to work on breathing techniques. It's very difficult to sit in a corner and meditate. I tried so hard, but it wasn't easy. It took too much effort, and honestly, every last drop of energy I had was being used to take care of my daughter.

I needed a form of meditation that required no energy from me. In the months and years following this very stressful experience, that's exactly what I found and began to practice.

## MEDITATION FOR PEOPLE WHO THINK THEY CAN'T MEDITATE

If you've ever tried meditating on your own, you might have some preconceived notions about meditating and think there's no way that you can do it. Maybe you've even given up. If that's the case, try yoga nidra. It is a completely different experience, and my favorite type of meditation to practice and teach.

You simply lie down on your back for the length of the session while a meditation teacher guides you through a series of mental exercises and visualizations that lead to a deep state of relaxation.

Even though you may appear to be sleeping to a quick observer, you are actually awake and hovering in a state of consciousness that's somewhere between waking and sleeping. The body benefits from the deepest levels of rest while the mind remains conscious.

What makes yoga nidra so effective during stressful times is that you don't have to do anything but lie down, close your eyes, and listen to the teacher's voice. You don't have to know how to control your breath or clear your mind. Once I started listening to yoga nidra recordings a couple of times a week, I found that it was a great addition to my toolbox to live my best life and combat stress.

I highly recommend that you begin managing your everyday ongoing stress with a yoga nidra meditation once or twice a week. Have this in your back pocket as a tool in the event of unexpected acute stress. If you know what to do and have a plan in place, you'll find that even your most acute stress is a little more manageable.

You can search locally for yoga studios or meditation centers that teach yoga nidra, or you can look online for pre-recorded sessions that you can listen to while you lie in bed or on a yoga mat.

Once you listen to a few yoga nidra sessions, you'll begin to notice that many teachers use a similarly structured framework. Using this framework, you can begin to understand how to achieve peace even when you don't have a recording at your fingertips.

Here is an abbreviated yoga nidra-inspired exercise that you can commit to memory and try anywhere:

**Step 1:**
Lie down on your back with your eyes closed and arms alongside your body with your palms facing up. Take a few moments to become still and notice the sounds in your space.

**Step 2:**
Keeping your eyes closed, bring your awareness to the space between your eyebrows. Gaze into this space and create a short, positive resolve (sankalpa). The sankalpa reflects your heart's true desire and is a statement that is meant to guide you and encourage positive change in your life. Create a sankalpa that is stated in the present tense and repeat it in your head three times to absorb and internalize this idea.

Some examples of short resolves include:

o   I am healthy
o   I am strong
o   I am confident

## Step 3:

The next phase of yoga nidra is called "rotation of consciousness" and involves bringing awareness to different parts of the body in a systematic way. Although you do not have an instructor to call out each body part, you can still relax the body by bringing your mental awareness to different parts of the body and holding your focus on each body part for about three seconds.

Begin by bringing your awareness to your right thumb, and then to the other fingers of your right hand. Make your way up the right arm (forearm, elbow, upper arm, armpit), and then make your way down the length of your right side, as you bring awareness to your right waist, hip, thigh, knee, calf, and foot.

Complete your rotation of consciousness on the right side by bringing your awareness to each toe of your right foot. Repeat this exercise on the left side of your body.

## Step 4:

Once you are done with rotation of consciousness, move on to this breathing exercise. Bring your awareness to your breath and notice how your belly rises with each inhale and falls with each exhale. Count each inhale and exhale, beginning with the number 27. Count backwards and make your way down to the number one.

Count like this: 27 belly up, 27 belly down. 26 belly up, 26 belly down. If you lose count, just start all over again at 27.

**Step 5:**

Finally, bring your awareness back into the space between your eyebrows, and end your self-guided yoga nidra by mentally repeating your sankalpa three times.

When you are done, you can slowly move each finger and toe to bring awareness back into your body. Slowly open your eyes and take a few moments to enjoy the benefits of your relaxing practice.

## REFLECTIONS & OBSERVATIONS:

<u>DAY 1:</u>

List the various aspects of your life that cause you stress. Do you suspect that this stress is affecting your physical body? What do you hope to gain from this Builder?

_____

_____

_____

_____

_____

_____

_____

<u>One Week Check-In:</u>

Now that you've begun a meditation practice, how do you feel? Did you notice an immediate effect after your first session? Is this a lifestyle habit that you'd like to maintain? Do you feel ready to incorporate another Builder into your life?

_____

_____

_____

_____

_____

_____

_____

## Chapter 15

# THE SWEET FEELING OF PRODUCTIVITY

If you are a naturally driven person and productivity is very important to you, I know how difficult it must be for you to deal with a chronic illness. On the days when your illness unpredictably flares up, you feel useless to the world because you aren't well enough to engage in your usual daily activities. It's demoralizing to cancel plans or to be unable to work, cook, or take care of your family.

The purpose of this Builder is to instill a small sense of productivity into your life each day by working on a mind-stimulating activity with an end goal.

When you are feeling well, you might not even appreciate the benefit of this exercise. But when you are facing tough days, this Builder will be surprisingly effective at making you feel productive and content.

**Builder #4: Exercise your brain with an activity that has an end goal.**

Just as it's important to exercise your body, it's also important to exercise your mind on a regular basis. Find an activity that requires focus, that you enjoy, and that you can do in 15-minute blocks of time.

You are welcome to spend longer, but 15-minutes is the minimum amount of time that you should engage in your chosen activity.

## THE IMPORTANCE OF SMALL GOALS

When you have a chronic illness, one of the greatest stumbling blocks is having a rough stretch of pain and discomfort that leaves you feeling awful and unable to get through your usual life routine. Productivity goes out the window when you're feeling bad, and unfortunately, that often leads to an emotional slump.

The idea behind this Builder is rooted in something far deeper than just keeping your mind sharp. Yes, that's one benefit, but the true purpose is to immerse yourself in an activity that gives you a sense of productivity and a feeling of working toward an end goal. This is a way of staying productive and keeping your mindset positive, even if it's a day that you're not feeling so well.

I discovered firsthand that it didn't take a whole lot to restore my sense of pride and accomplishment when I was knocked out of commission. I didn't need to run a company successfully, smash fitness goals, or even manage my household efficiently.

A small project with an end goal was enough to get my mind focused and feeling useful. As I approached my goal—even if that goal was finishing a 500-piece jigsaw puzzle—I felt good!

## SUGGESTIONS TO EXPLORE

Today, I'm not struggling with my autoimmune condition, but I continue to keep my spirits up by always having a mind-stimulating project or puzzle running in the background of my life. I enjoy it as a hobby, and I feel good knowing that it will make a difference on days when I'm struggling and feeling sick.

Currently, I am researching immigration documents and census reports from the early 1900s to build my family tree using an online service. Every time I discover a new connection to my family, I feel a tremendous sense of accomplishment. I feel like I'm working toward an end goal at all times, and that is stimulating and gratifying.

Here are a few other ideas that you can incorporate into your own life. Some are short-lived exercises that can be completed in one sitting, and others are longer-term projects. See what sounds appealing and give it a try.

o   Crossword puzzles

o   Sudoku

o   Word searches

o   Adult coloring books

o   Learning to play a musical instrument

o   Playing chess, Othello, poker, or another game that requires strategy. (You can download an app that allows you to play against the computer and move on to more difficult levels after each successful game.)

o   Studying a new language

## THE VALUE OF A LONGER-TERM PROJECT

I'm a fan of the longer-term projects, like studying a new language or learning to play an instrument. These are examples of larger undertakings that can be accomplished in small bite-sized chunks.

These are also projects where you can move the end goal as you progress. Once you learn the basics of communicating in new language or playing a simple song on an instrument, you can set the bar higher.

If the idea of learning a new language sounds fun to you, look for online courses that you can do in short increments right on your phone or computer. If you prefer the idea of learning an instrument, schedule a few classes with a local teacher to learn the basics of reading music and handling the instrument of your choice.

## TALKING POINTS

One bonus that emerges from taking on these projects is that you suddenly have an interesting topic to discuss with family and friends. It's refreshing to talk about something besides your personal health and aches and pains.

Even though I know you are battling every day, you don't want to give the illness too much energy by discussing it repeatedly. You want to fill as many of your waking hours with positive thoughts and conversations and leave very little room for negative thoughts or complaints.

## PUT A LIMIT ON GRIPING

If you must talk about your physical ailments, put a time limit on it, especially if you are in a group setting. Complaining about pain and discomfort is oddly contagious and somehow makes its way around a whole room.

Before you know it, everyone's been talking about aches and pains for over an hour. If a health discussion is necessary, announce (with humor) that the medical gripes discussion will be limited to one minute per person.

You are more than your illness and more than your collection of aching body parts. You have more to offer your friends and family than your list of pains. Go ahead and share your new endeavor with them and pass the inspiration along.

## REFLECTIONS & OBSERVATIONS:

DAY 1:

How important is productivity to you? When your illness prevents you from getting through your usual daily responsibilities and routines, what happens to your mental state? What mind-stimulating projects would you like to begin?

_____

_____

_____

_____

_____

_____

_____

One Week Check-In:

How do you feel after a week of working on your project or puzzle? Did you feel a sense of purpose and accomplishment as you worked each day? Will you continue with this Builder? Are you ready to incorporate another Builder into your life?

_____

_____

_____

_____

_____

_____

_____

## Chapter 16

# CREATE INSTANT PEACE

This next exercise will give you a sense of instant gratification. I know that so much of this journey is a process that requires patience. Thriving takes time. Fortunately, this activity is one where the benefits are immediate. Do it today, and your mind will feel clearer, and your creative juices will be flowing in no time.

Summon your energy and take on Builder #5.

**Builder #5: Clear a horizontal surface in your house.**

Declutter any flat surface in your house that can serve as a tabletop. Remove everything that's resting on the surface and wipe it down so that it's clean. This can be a desk, a dining table, a kitchen counter or island with stools, or a bar top. Just make sure that it's a large enough surface for work or hobbies.

The idea is to create one permanently decluttered flat space where your eyes and mind can rest each time you walk into the room.

By clearing off a single surface (including all decorative items and plants), you will have a place in your home that will always feel like a respite—a refreshing place where you can write, read your books, and do something creative.

A blank slate.

A place where a greater vision for your life can emerge.

When spaces at home are cluttered, it's mentally draining to imagine tackling any kind of task. There's no creative vision because there's no room to think.

If your cluttered tabletop makes it difficult to pay bills or write a birthday card, how can any greater vision be sparked in that space? How can you envision conquering your illness? Controlling your symptoms? Achieving your personal, professional, or wellness goals?

You are trying to thrive. You cannot risk having your spirit and energy dampened in any way, especially not from something as fixable as a messy tabletop. We may not have control over a lot of things in life, but we certainly can control the clutter on a single flat surface.

Take a look around your house and pick a table to tackle. If it's covered with papers, mail, permission slips from school, receipts, plates, cups, and trinkets, how does that make you feel? Exhausted? Cloudy? Chaotic? Depressed? Overwhelmed?

I don't know which of these descriptive words resonates with you, but I will boldly say that none of these words seem particularly positive to me.

You do not have to spring clean your entire home. I'm asking you to pick one flat surface in your house and clear it off completely. My hope is that the effect is so dramatic that you will be tempted to attack another surface, and then a drawer—maybe even a full closet or office space after that!

## THE QUICK AND EASY SOLUTION

I know that your energy levels have improved since completing the 40-day program of Boosters, but I also know that your health is unpredictable. Instead of cleaning your flat surface by removing one item at a time and finding a new home for each of the items that currently resides on your table, grab a laundry basket or a decorative container.

Sweep all the items into your basket so you can begin to enjoy the impact of a decluttered surface immediately. If you have the energy, go ahead and figure out the fate of each item in your basket. If you can't do it all at once, put it aside and deal with it in short bursts.

Right now, I just want you to experience the clarity and rejuvenation of having access to an uncluttered, completely clean surface for your work and pleasure. My hope for you is that you can maintain it as a clear space indefinitely so that you can see the long-term benefits of having such a space in your house.

## REFLECTIONS & OBSERVATIONS:

<u>DAY 1:</u>

Compare how you feel before and after you clear off your flat surface. What can you imagine yourself doing on this empty canvas of space? What will you do to ensure that this space remains free of clutter?

_____

_____

_____

_____

_____

_____

_____

<u>One Week Check-In:</u>

Have you been able to maintain a clean and decluttered space all week? Did the new work space inspire any new activities or hobbies? Did the clean surface spark feelings of clarity, motivation or rejuvenation? Write your feelings below. Which Builder are you planning to try next?

_____

_____

_____

_____

_____

_____

_____

## Chapter 17

# ESCAPE PLAN

A change is as good as a rest. That's what my father used to say to me every time he saw me struggling for many hours to write a paper for school. He wasn't suggesting that I stop working altogether, but he was suggesting that I work on something completely different to clear my head.

When I listened to him, I found that I was much more effective with my work. I would return to the original paper a while later to find that my mind was clear, and I was able to write sections of the paper that had me stumped a few hours earlier.

It's amazing how rejuvenating it is to just change gears. Doing something different is often just as effective as taking a break and doing nothing. That is the thought behind this next Builder.

**Builder #6: Schedule time once a quarter to escape the struggles of everyday life.**

First off, there's nothing wrong with doing nothing, and if that's what sounds most appealing to you, schedule it as your quarterly escape.

Doing something that's a complete change in your routine is also just as effective for your mental health as lying on a beach and doing nothing. You can attend a conference on a topic that interests you, or volunteer for a project or trip through a local charitable organization. Either of these ventures—even though they require energy—can be as rejuvenating for your spirit as flying away to a deserted tropical island.

An escape can be a vacation, but you can find many ways to escape the monotony of daily life, even if you stay close to home. The length of your escape will obviously depend on your means and your availability, but the point is making it part of your lifestyle by doing it every three months.

## WHY EVERY THREE MONTHS?

Twenty years ago, I accepted my first job right out of college at a big investment bank. They gave me four weeks of vacation each year. I was really surprised by this generous vacation policy, and I remember asking my boss why we were given so many days. He said the company believed that everyone should have one full week off per quarter to rejuvenate and avoid burnout.

I thought this was interesting because this was also a company that didn't mind if I consistently worked 90 hours a week to get my work done. It was a culture of taking on as much as you could bear and then taking a seriously deserved break.

Doesn't the "taking-on-as-much-as-you-could-bear" part sound familiar? It reminds me so much of life with a chronic illness! On top of normal everyday responsibilities, you also carry the weight of a medical condition that can flare-up at any time and turns everyday responsibilities into exhausting hurdles. You're forced to take on as much as you can bear, and that's just not sustainable for any length of time. You need a change of scenery and a solid break from your everyday routine.

Twenty years later, I'm no longer working at the investment bank, but I continue to subscribe to their vacation policy and always look forward to some sort of special escape every three months. It's just the right length of time to shake up the routine and get out of a funk if I'm falling into one.

So, what kind of escape would you like to begin planning?

## MAKE IT SPECIAL

You can plan a vacation, organize a spa day with friends, book a dinner cruise, take a helicopter tour, go camping, volunteer your time for a good cause, or attend a festival. These are just a few suggestions, but it doesn't really matter what you choose as long as it's vastly different from your day-to-day life.

The point is to do something special that will have the same lasting effects as taking a rejuvenating vacation.

Ideally, we would all be flying to the exotic destination of our choice, but this isn't necessarily realistic. If your budget allows you to take a big trip every three months, then go for it. If you can't, you can certainly find an escape that's closer to home and just as impactful.

Just be sure to go on your quarterly escape and begin planning the next one as soon as it's over. Three months can fly by in a flash, and you don't want to suddenly realize that you have nothing planned. Part of the joy of a vacation or a special escape is the anticipation. You want to draw that excitement out as much as possible.

If you begin planning your trip a week before you take it, you don't have a long stretch of time to savor the building excitement and anticipation. The escape itself is most important, but the building anticipation of all of the fun you'll have is also a big source of joy. That joy, in turn, is an important part of being able to thrive on your chronic illness journey.

## REFLECTIONS & OBSERVATIONS:

DAY 1:

If you are planning quarterly escapes, decide which months make most sense for your schedule, and write them down below. Think about your budget. Can any of the escapes include overnight expenses for travel and hotel? If your escapes will be close to home, what sorts of activities do you want to try? Make sure that your plans are vastly different from your day-to-day life.

_____

_____

_____

_____

_____

_____

_____

Quarterly Check-In:

Did you take your first quarterly escape? Was it energizing? Relaxing? Rejuvenating? Are you looking forward to scheduling and planning your next escape? Did you learn anything about yourself during the escape?

_____

_____

_____

_____

_____

_____

_____

# Chapter 18

# EXTERIOR WORK

Most of our focus so far has been on mood-boosting tasks that require us to transform on the inside. This next Builder will also lift our spirits, but the main focus is on doing work on the outside—on our physical bodies.

This will require a little bit of research, exploration, and monetary investment on your part. I can't tell you what's best for your body, but I'm confident that you have the energy and spirit to figure out what's likely to work best.

Schedule time in your life to find the treatment that will help you maintain good health when you have it and help you feel better when you don't.

**Builder #7: Explore different types of bodywork.**

Bodywork is a term used to describe many kinds of therapeutic treatments and relaxing practices. Moxibustion, acupuncture, acupressure, reflexology, reiki, cupping, deep tissue massage, and shiatsu are just a few examples of bodywork that are available to you to aid the body in natural healing.

With the right treatment and the right therapist, bodywork can improve your mood, relieve stress, correct imbalances in your body, and alleviate pain. It's your job to figure out which treatment is the most beneficial for your body.

Some types of bodywork are very hands-on experiences where a trained practitioner actively touches you, either with their own hands, needles, or glass cups. Others can be classified as energy work and require very little touch. Some healing treatments, like moxibustion, can be practiced at home on your own. There's a lot to explore.

## GETTING STARTED

Begin by calling your insurance company to see if any bodywork sessions are covered by your plan. You might get lucky. Some insurance plans cover acupuncture sessions or massage sessions that are booked at physical therapy centers.

If your budget allows (or if your insurance plan covers it), massage can become a regular part of your wellness routine. Other treatments like acupuncture or moxibustion can be used once in a while to alleviate pain and discomfort. It's nice to have some options in your back pocket for when you're feeling lousy and want to take action to feel better.

How do you know what type of body work is right for you? Well, as with anything else in life, you have to experiment a bit and keep an open mind. If you know that your body hurts too much to be touched, skip the very hands-on approaches like deep tissue massage. You can consider reiki, which is a form of energy therapy and doesn't require moving the skin around. Acupuncture or moxibustion, which require minimal touch, are also possibilities to explore.

When the drugs aren't working and the medical treatments seem ineffective, alternative healing methods might be the solution.

Not everything in the world is yet understood, and that's particularly true for some of these ancient healing techniques that have been used for thousands of years. Just because it's not understood doesn't mean that it's not real.

## THE DAY I BECAME A BELIEVER

I was introduced to the power of acupuncture several years ago when I went to an acupuncturist for relief from Lyme disease symptoms.

Acupuncture is an ancient Chinese treatment that involves putting needles into your skin at various points on the body in order to move energy flow, known as qi. I didn't like the idea of being stuck with needles and felt tremendous anxiety about the whole process, but I was in a lot of pain and willing to try anything.

I had been experiencing sharp lower back pain for years that was getting progressively worse, most likely as a result of systemic inflammation caused by my illness. Before turning to acupuncture, I had been treated with traction, electric stimulation, heat, ice, exercise, manual therapy, ultrasound, and various rock taping techniques.

Because these methods were not very effective at relieving my pain, I was skeptical that acupuncture would be the treatment that suddenly worked for me. I decided to give it a try anyway, so I pushed passed my fears and scheduled my first acupuncture session.

As expected, the acupuncturist placed needles all over my body, not just at the site of the pain, but also in my ears, arms, ankles, and feet.

It was not a comfortable experience, but I managed to doze off on the table for some period of time. After the acupuncturist roused me from my little nap, she removed the needles and told me that I could get dressed.

I will never forget the moment when I sat up. I had no back pain. I was stunned. Years of back pain disappeared in just one acupuncture session. My mind was blown. The acupuncturist explained something about increasing blood flow to the SI (sacroiliac) joint and unblocking meridians, but I was in shock and didn't catch everything she said.

She wasn't surprised by my pain relief because she helped people all the time, but I was totally stunned. It's funny that to this day, I continue to be surprised by the miracles of natural and alternative healing techniques, even though I know firsthand that they work.

## FROM ACUPUNCTURE TO MOXA

These days, I rarely get acupuncture treatments, but I've learned how to use moxibustion (also called moxa) to treat myself at home. I like to think of moxa as a more accessible form of acupuncture to an individual practitioner.

There's no way that I would try putting needles into my own skin, but moxa, which also works like acupuncture by moving the flow of qi, is a less intimidating process.

Moxa is a type of heat therapy that involves burning a small cone or stick of ground mugwort leaves along various meridian points on the body. You can think of meridians as energy channels that run through the body, and each meridian is associated with the health of an internal organ.

Once you learn about the body's meridian system and get guidance on how to use moxa, it's quite simple to do at home. Find a teacher that can give you a moxa lesson. If you're having trouble finding a teacher locally, you can reach out to a knowledgeable healer online who might be able to offer you a lesson via video chat.

You'll pay for the initial session to learn the basics, but after that, it's an economical form of bodywork because your only cost will be the moxa, which you can buy from on online source.

## NEVER STOP LEARNING

In my own journey, I've found it really beneficial to my mental health as well as my physical health, to be a constant learner. It's important to stay intellectually curious. Read up on new treatments to see if there's something else that might improve how you feel each day. This will boost your sense of purpose and your sense of hope.

Every treatment won't work for every condition, but keep dabbling and you'll find something effective. Remember that it may take multiple sessions to notice a difference. Don't dismiss anything as ineffective until you work with a particular treatment and therapist a few times.

I truly believe that you have far more control over how you feel than you've been led to believe. Don't give up. Keep exploring and trying new things.

## REFLECTIONS & OBSERVATIONS:

DAY 1:

Are you interested in alternative healing modalities? If so, what do you want to explore first? Do you have any reservations? Write your thoughts and expectations below.

_____

_____

_____

_____

_____

_____

Post-Treatment Check-In:

Describe your first body treatment. How did you feel during the treatment, and how do you feel now that it's over? Will you make this type of treatment a regular part of your wellness plan? If not, will you try another type of body treatment?

_____

_____

_____

_____

_____

_____

## Chapter 19

# CATCH GOOD VIBES LIKE THEY ARE CONTAGIOUS

The final Builder is meant to leave you with a smile on your face. Energy is contagious. If you surround yourself with negative, sour energy, you'll notice that your own energy levels will become depressed to match. Surround yourself with happy, bright energy instead, and you'll find your own energy levels rising, too.

As soon as you feel well enough, embrace this next Builder. Do it as often as you can and know that your life will be richer because of it.

**Builder #8: Spend more time with the happiest people you know.**

We can all think of a couple of people in our lives that just make us smile. Maybe it's because of their bubbly personality or upbeat outlook on life. It's hard to pinpoint exactly what it is, but we know that we feel better when we are around them. They are good for our souls because they exude good energy and life.

These are the people that you need to be around. They might be old friends, new friends, colleagues, or little children. There are no parameters on who makes you happy. You know who these people are.

Spend more time with them because their enthusiasm for life will rub off on you. It's not possible to be around happy people without creating some of our own feel-good vibes in the process. These feel-good vibes are so important in helping us create the kind of lives that we want to live.

I have a friend in my life that is so bubbly and full of life that I actually forget about my pain when I'm with her. Well…maybe I don't completely forget, but her personality is so big that it turns the volume down on my pain to the point that it's not something that I even want to mention. I'm more active when I'm with her, and I'm happier than my usual baseline of happiness. It's amazing how a positive spirit can help us thrive.

Spending more time with your happy crowd doesn't mean that you have to abandon your friends who are struggling or going through a rough season at the moment. All it means is that you are allocating a bit more time to the folks who bring a smile to your face, motivate you, and inspire you to want more for your own life.

Remember that these happy people also want to be around people who feed their souls and make them happy. Make sure to do your part. Talk about your new routines. Tell them about your social media fast, the books you are reading, and the podcasts that you have found. Don't focus on your pain and complaints when you're with them. Use your time with these sources of light to kindle your own flame.

# REFLECTIONS & OBSERVATIONS:

DAY 1:

Make a list of the people in your life that make you happy. How can you schedule more time with them? Make a list of possibilities, whether it's a weekly meet-up for coffee or an extra conversation on the phone each week. Be intentional with your time so that you are sure to spend time with these happy people.

_____

_____

_____

_____

_____

_____

One Week Check-In:

Did you find ways to spend more time with your favorite happy people this week? How did you feel afterwards? Did you notice a shift in your mood? Will you make an effort each week to spend time with someone who lifts your spirit?

_____

_____

_____

_____

_____

_____

# BUILDERS CHEAT SHEET

After 40 days of Boosters, your energy levels will be higher, and you'll be ready to add Builders into your life.

Builders are the healthy lifestyle habits that will form the foundation of your newly inspired life.

Add one Builder to your routine, get used to it for a week, and then consider adding another. Incorporate your favorites, and don't worry about the rest. This is the beginning of the rest of your life!

1. Move your body, but in a pain-free zone.

2. Pick a diet to follow that promises to heal your body.

3. Develop a regular meditation practice to manage stress.

4. Exercise your brain with an activity that has an end goal.

5. Clear a horizontal surface in your house.

6. Schedule time once every three months to escape the struggles of everyday life.

7. Explore different types of bodywork.

8. Spend more time with the happiest people you know.

*Section Three*

# TROUBLESHOOTING & FINAL THOUGHTS

*Chapter 20*

# ADHERENCE TO THE PROGRAM

Once you finish reading this book, you must ask yourself whether you are serious about staying on track and applying what you've learned to your life. Are you ready to commit to the 40-day program?

If you are serious and ready, think about what you need to do from a practical standpoint to be successful.

How will you remember all eight Boosters that you need to do each day, and how will you keep track of which tasks you've completed? Are you going to carry this book everywhere and flip through each chapter? Probably not. That doesn't sound very convenient. You need a plan to stay accountable—a system to remind you of your daily tasks, and a way of tracking the ones that you complete.

## HOW TO REMEMBER THE BOOSTERS

First, let's tackle the dilemma of remembering all eight Boosters. That's a tough one, but you know what always works for me when I'm trying to remember large amounts of information? Using an acronym.

If you can remember the phrase "BE ACTIVE," you will be able to remember all eight Boosters, albeit in a different order than they were presented in the book. Each letter in the phrase "BE ACTIVE" is a reminder of a Booster that you need to complete for the day.

**B**edtime routine

**E**liminate social media

**A**ir (open a window or get outside)

**C**ompliments

**T**hankfulness practice (make a list!)

**I**nspirational media (books, blogs, podcasts)

**V**isualization (picture the life you want)

**E**liminate sugar and highly processed foods

Now that you have this convenient acronym to remember your daily tasks, here are three suggestions for tracking the Boosters as you complete them each day:

## USE A TO-DO LIST APP

If you are tech savvy and enjoy keeping track of your life electronically, download a to-do list app onto your phone. An app like this will allow you to make checklists for all of your daily tasks and habits.

There are numerous programs out there that you can research and download. Wunderlist, Google Tasks, Productive Habit Tracker, and Microsoft To-Do are just a few examples of the many to-do list apps that are available. You can put all eight Boosters into one of these programs, and each day, mark off your Boosters as you complete them. Since your phone most likely goes where you go, you'll always have your Boosters with you.

## WRITE A TO-DO LIST EACH NIGHT

If you prefer the good old-fashioned method of putting pen to paper, you can skip the app, and just write your Boosters on a sheet of paper every night before going to bed. Make this part of your bedtime routine so that you are mentally prepared for the next morning.

The following day, put a checkmark next to each task as you complete it. Even if it feels cumbersome to have to write a new list every evening, it's certainly a great way to internalize the process and reminding yourself of what needs to be done.

If you tend to be a visual learner or the type of learner that does best by writing things down, this method might be the most effective for you.

## CREATE YOUR OWN SPREADSHEET OR DOWNLOAD MINE

The third option is for those of you who love spreadsheets as much as I do. You can keep track of all 40 days of tasks in an easy-to-read grid. Every time you complete a task, you can check it off.

You can even make it a fun game by giving yourself a point for each completed task. Count your points for the day, week or month to quickly assess your adherence to the program.

If you like the idea of using a spreadsheet to keep track of your Boosters, I'd be happy to share my template with you. If you would like a copy for your own use, go to my website https://riseandthrivebooks.com/spreadsheet to download the file.

## MISSING A DAY (OR SIX)

Sometimes, we fall off track, and routines are broken. Life happens. If you find yourself in this situation, pick yourself up and re-start the 40-day program as if nothing happened.

That single missed day or missed week is not what determines whether you thrive. It's every other day of the year that determines your fate.

I've structured the program to have a 40-day timeframe because that's how long it takes to make thriving a habit. That's how long it takes to shift your mindset so that you are consistently making choices in your life that are in line with your greatest dreams for yourself.

At the end of 40 days, you continue your daily Boosters anyway. It's a lifestyle. You don't fail because you completed 36 consecutive days of Boosters and then missed days 37 and 38. You weren't going to stop at day 40 anyway! Forty is just a milestone. This plan is the launch pad for the rest of your life. If you miss a few days, don't beat yourself up. Don't stress. Just keep going.

In the next chapter, we will talk about managing your worst days. It's not a fun topic, but it's a necessary one. Let's discuss what you can do to get through these rough times so that you can get back to business of living a vibrant, inspired life.

*Chapter 21*

# MANAGING YOUR TOUGH DAYS

Despite all your best efforts to incorporate daily rituals and healthy habits into your life, you may find yourself in a situation where your illness rears its ugly head and knocks you out of commission. It's discouraging to have these extreme episodes of pain and exhaustion, but you must remind yourself that it's temporary.

## WORST-CASE SCENARIO

I know from personal experience that some flare-ups are so awful that you can't even open your eyes to read, watch TV, or talk to anyone. If this is what you find yourself up against, then rest.

Forget your Boosters and Builders. They aren't going anywhere. The only thing on your to-do list is to sleep and get as much rest as possible. That's all there is to do when you are completely debilitated.

## THE GRAY AREA

If you've been living with a chronic illness for a while, you know that flare-ups tend to exist on a spectrum. "Debilitating" is on one end of the spectrum, and "not so bad" is on the other end. There's a whole lot of gray area in the middle.

I hope you spend most of your days hovering on the "not so bad" end of the spectrum, but if you know that you tend to find yourself in the gray area from time to time, make sure that you're prepared for those days. There's a lot that you can do today to make tough times easier.

## HAVE A PLAN

It's all much easier to manage if you have a game plan in place ahead of time. Think about your life and jot down a quick list of responsibilities that must be accounted for immediately if you're unable to do them. Really boil down your list to the essentials. Chances are, you'll realize that you only have to consider three broad categories:

o Work
o Family/pets
o Meals

## WORK

If you work, you'll need to know who to call if you will be unable to make it in for a period of time. Schedule a meeting talk to your boss or someone in Human Resources and explain your medical condition and the unpredictability of your pain. They will be able to advise you of company policies and benefits under the Family and Medical Leave Act.

Try to be as specific as you can about your physical capabilities on bad days. If it tends to be variable, disclose that. Sometimes, you might be well enough to work from home and be fully available via phone and e-mail, and other times, you might not be able to work at all. It all depends on the severity of the flare-up.

I've discovered that most people don't know a lot about chronic conditions, autoimmune diseases, or anything that falls under the umbrella designation of "invisible illness." It's hard to imagine that a healthy looking, able-bodied person can be fine on Monday and then in terrible pain on Tuesday.

It's in your best interest to educate others when you are feeling well so that you aren't answering a lot of questions and feeling the skepticism on the day that you call out sick. If everyone is on the same page ahead of time, you won't be on the phone having difficult conversations on the day you call out sick with a mystery illness.

If a colleague will be covering for you while you are out, think about doing something nice for them to show your appreciation once you are back at work. It doesn't have to be an expensive gesture—treating your colleague to an afternoon cup of coffee or tea is perfect.

## FAMILY AND PETS

When it comes to your kids and pets, decide today who will take care of your kids if you are unable to care for them yourself.

How will your kids get to school?

Who will pick them up?

How will they get to and from after-school activities?

Who will help them with their homework?

If you have babies or toddlers at home, who can come help?

Do you have anyone that can feed and take care of your pets?

These questions need answers, and the solutions must be in place now.

If you have a family member that can help you, then make sure they are fully on board today so that you aren't stressed on the day that you wake up and realize you aren't well.

If you don't have a family member that can help you, enlist help from friends and neighbors, or start developing a relationship with a babysitter that can help.

## MEALS

Finally, let's discuss meals. If you are managing your autoimmune condition with a very specific diet, it can be really stressful to have a flare-up and be unable to stand in the kitchen to prepare food in the exact way that you think is most beneficial.

I understand. I spent years managing my rheumatological symptoms with a strict macrobiotic diet that required a lot of food preparation. As my diet revolved around whole grains, beans, and vegetables, I spent a lot of time washing, chopping, cooking, and soaking.

On most days, it was a lot of work, but I was fine because I had energy and no pain. But what happened on the rare occasion that I had a sudden inflammatory attack of my hands, wrists, knees, or foot?

I was unable to do everything that I needed to do to prepare the food I needed to eat for my condition.

I felt awful about breaking away from my very regimented healing diet, but it just didn't work for me on my worst days. I didn't feel well enough to be in the kitchen for extended periods of time.

## KEEPING IT SIMPLE

I needed an easy solution for when it was too difficult to stay on track with my usual routine. That's when I decided to dial my perfectionist nature down a notch.

If I was in the middle of a painful flare-up, I didn't need elaborate meals with every food group represented on my plate. I could make a single large pot of quinoa and eat it for three days straight with some lettuce leaves or raw bok choy right out of the refrigerator.

And that's exactly what I did.

Was it boring to eat the same thing repeatedly, day after day? Yes. But this plan allowed me to get through my hardest days without resorting to random bags of chips and cookies in my pantry. Not only that, but I managed to eat meals that were healthy.

On my worst days, I was back at Booster #3—eating simply prepared foods with no added sugar. When you're not feeling well, everything has to be easy.

If you're in a situation where cooking of any kind is out of the question, call your local Chinese restaurant. They usually deliver, and it's the one kind of take-out restaurant where you can be sure to find assorted steamed vegetables. Ask for simply prepared foods with all sauces on the side.

If you have a family and need to consider their meals too, make it as easy as possible on yourself. On your worst days, serve cereal for breakfast, let the kids buy lunch at school, and order pizza for dinner.

No, this isn't a long-term plan, but you will be able to get through your toughest days. Your family will survive on convenience foods for a couple of days until you are on your feet again.

## HOW TO START PREPARING TODAY

The important thing to do right now is to get your plan in place. Start cooking your dinners in double batches and freeze half so that they can be quickly defrosted when you have just enough energy to heat food in a pot.

You can find lots of recipes for dinners that freeze well, like pasta sauces and soups. Cook in bulk so that you have fairly easy options on days when your energy levels are low.

If your flare-ups are few and far between, eat your freezer meals throughout the month and just keep replacing them. You will not waste food or waste time. You will feel better knowing that you have a plan in place for your meals if the time ever comes that you need them.

# Chapter 22

# TIME TO SHINE

Several years ago, I attended a conference, and one of the speakers gave some great advice about improving relationships. I know this isn't a book about relationships, but I thought this advice was relevant to all aspects of life, and I'd like to share it with you.

Here's the advice:

Step 1. Draw an imaginary circle on the ground.
Step 2. Step inside the circle.
Step 3. Work on everyone in that circle.

That's it! Internalize these three, simple steps and watch your life transform.

This visualization emphasizes that all change begins with you. If you want a sense of peace, you must stop worrying about what everyone else is doing or thinking and start working on yourself. Thriving begins in your own mind, not in external validation.

Living with a chronic illness and managing symptoms is a roller coaster experience. Sometimes you're high on a peak, and sometimes you are down in a valley. As long as you know how to consistently pick yourself up and get out of that valley feeling motivated and excited to live, your illness won't win. You will.

So, as you continue on your own individual healing journey, know that you have the power to cultivate the positive mindset needed to thrive and live a fulfilling, exciting life.

- o Practice your eight Boosters on a daily basis.

- o Incorporate as many of the eight Builders as you can into your life.

- o Remember that you are not in competition with anyone, so stop comparing yourself to others.

- o Stop comparing yourself to previous versions of yourself.

- o Live in the present.

- o Set an intention to do your best every day, but recognize that your best effort might be different each day.

And if you're too sick to do anything, forgive yourself. Treat yourself like you would treat a sick friend—without judgment or anger.

Above all, know that you are not alone. We may all be managing different chronic illnesses, but we are connected in our desire to feel well so that we can do more and be more.

If you would like to connect with me, you can reach me at masumi@riseandthrivebooks.com.

# ABOUT THE AUTHOR

**MASUMI GOLDMAN** is a former Wall Street analyst and MIT graduate who wandered into the world of wellness in order to manage a painful condition that affected her joints and tendons. She has made it a habit to rise to every challenge and thrive, whether that's been in a chemistry lab, on a trading floor, teaching yoga in large conference settings, or advocating for herself in her multiyear journey with Lyme disease.

Her passion for yoga, meditation, and all things wellness-related sparked a successful blog, multiple yoga certifications, and numerous features in various media outlets. She has partnered with major brands, such as Gaiam and Kohl's in their wellness endeavors and helped launch two separate yoga apparel lines, yoga DVDs and a series of downloadable yoga classes. She has also contributed to wellness publications, including *Yoga Journal*, *Shape*, *NY Yoga + Life Magazine*, and *Yoga Digest*.

For more information, visit https://riseandthrivebooks.com.

# Can You Help?

Thanks so much for taking the time to read my book! I hope you are inspired to move forward, despite the challenges you face each day.

If you enjoyed this book and found it to be valuable to your own wellness journey, I would love to hear from you. Please leave me a review on Amazon with your thoughts and ideas.

Thank you for your support,

Masumi Goldman

# Get Your FREE Gift Now!

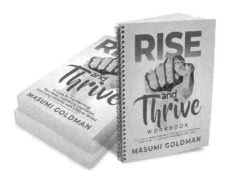

As a gift for buying my book, I would like to give you the
*Rise and Thrive Workbook.*

Your FREE workbook includes printable journaling pages and a
checklist with 40 additional tips to continue thriving.

## GET YOUR WORKBOOK HERE:

https://riseandthrivebooks.com/workbook